THE UNTAPPED RESOURCE
MEDICINE AND DIPLOMACY

THE UNTAPPED
RESOURCE

Edited and presented by

Kevin M. Cahill, M.D.

ORBIS
BOOKS
MARYKNOLL, NEW YORK

Some of the papers in this collection were presented in a
symposium sponsored by the Tropical Disease Center, St.
Clare's Hospital, N.Y., and the Merck Company Foundation, December 13, 1969, and subsequently published in the
Bulletin of the New York Academy of Medicine, May 1970.

Contributors

John S. Badeau, Director, The Middle East Institute; formerly
U. S. Ambassador to the United Arab Republic

Angie Brooks, President, The United Nations General Assembly
(24th Session)

Kevin M. Cahill, M.D., Director, The Tropical Disease Center,
New York; Professor and Chairman of Tropical Medicine,
Royal College of Surgeons in Ireland

Hugh L. Carey, United States Congressman; member Ways and
Means Committee; former member of the Commission on
Health, Education and Welfare

Abdulrahim Abby Farah, Permanent Ambassador of Somalia to
the United Nations; Representative on Security Council;
and Chairman of Political Committee

George I. Lythcott, M.D., Associate Dean, Columbia University
College of Physicians and Surgeons, New York; formerly
Field Director of U.S. Smallpox Eradication Program in
West Africa

Mark Perlman, University Professor and Chairman of Economics,
University of Pittsburgh; Editor, *Journal of Economic
Literature;* and Professor of Health Economics, Johns
Hopkins Medical School

Edward E. Swanstrom, Director, The Catholic Relief Services,
New York; Chairman American Council of Voluntary
Agencies for Foreign Service

In memory of Eileen C. Carey

TABLE OF CONTENTS

THE UNTAPPED RESOURCE
MEDICINE AND DIPLOMACY

Medicine and Diplomacy

An Introduction

Kevin M. Cahill

M EDICINE IS ONE of the last, and certainly the most promising of the untapped resources of contemporary international diplomacy. That is the unqualified contention of this book, published at a critical time. The future of foreign assistance programs is being debated. Alternatives to unsuccessful approaches in international relations are being sought. Funds for international medical research are diminishing. A "new" diplomacy is emerging in an era of instant communications. It is to be hoped that we in the developed countries have the maturity, the wisdom and, if necessary, the courage to jettison the standard, rigidly pursued, and often unsuccessful practices of past foreign policy in order to seek new methods of presenting what is fine and decent in one nation to those in another. If life is a series of alternatives, then medicine represents a good one indeed.

In today's world of newly emerging nations and powerful ideological blocs, diplomacy is restricted by few traditions and assumes many unorthodox guises. As the nations of the Third World became independent, the Eastern and Western blocs wooed

1

them with every conceivable form of aid. Many new governments have consistently accepted these "grants" with a gratitude marked by a lingering suspicion that the giver covertly seeks only his own good. Thus, the foreign airport builder or road-maker may find his efforts cited as proof of the militaristic nature of his "colonialistic government." The agriculture attaché can be accused of destroying traditional farming methods, the dam-builder of flooding the land, and the teacher of indoctrinating or deluding the young.

Few areas of overseas aid are immune to these sensitivities and possible misinterpretations of recipient nations. Few forms of aid can be offered with the assurance that both donor and recipient countries would experience the dramatic impact of immediate benefit, as well as the long-term effect of hard-won mutual respect. Few projects can be completed with the assurance that later political changes will not confuse or diminish the good that was done. Medicine is a unique exception, especially in the Third World, where infectious diseases and epidemics remain the great scourges.

Medicine and diplomacy are neither strange nor recent partners. Ancient kings employed their physicians as ambassadors of good will. The trust, respect, and affection elicited by the professional medical man was not limited to his role in the relief of pain or the control of disease, but extended to those he represented— his nation and his people. In many modern nations at the time of independence the doctor and the clergyman were the only educated members of the community and played prominent roles in national and international affairs. In the United States six of the signers of the Declaration of Independence were physicians. The role of the doctor in politics and foreign affairs in Latin American and African nations is well known.

For many years the average citizen was content to relegate foreign affairs to the nebulous realms of the State Department. But that time is gone. No longer can foreign policy be the exclusive domain of striped-pants ambassadors and their staffs. Today, the masses in every nation forcefully project their feelings, and statesmen must be responsive to these demands. Today, the young, for example, insist upon involvement and only the most bemused statesman would reject the obviously sincere desire of youth to serve their fellow man. What is needed on every level is not only leadership and direction, but also motivation and understanding, since anyone working or even visiting in a foreign country becomes involved—willingly or unwillingly—in the political exchange of his native and host nations. Even those who remain at home are deeply involved in foreign policy, since their taxes pay for overseas programs and they elect legislators whose views on foreign policy are a crucial part of any political platform. The "diplomacy of the masses" is here to stay.

We all, then, have a deep involvement in foreign affairs and—whether we like it or not—heavy responsibilities to encourage and foster better international understanding; else we must be willing to face the inevitable consequences of future war, cold or hot: and further suffering and the sacrifice of human and material potential.

During the past decade I have had the privilege of intimate contact with numerous diplomatic efforts while being associated with and later directing American medical research teams working in tropical areas. From these experiences I became convinced that combining medicine and diplomacy represents a most natural vehicle for modern international communication. In Africa, for example, where the stability of governments is yet a rare phenomenon, my own medical work served to form a bond between several regimes. In one country I had the pleasure of working under three different governments, and caring for the prime ministers and leaders in all three. There have been times when these men have sought my assistance in transmitting highly confidential messages to leaders of the United States.

Physicians and medical workers have the unique opportunity and privilege of entering far more rapidly than can any other profession into the closed and often suspicious inner political circles and power structures of developing lands. Needless to say, this privilege brings responsibility and requires great sensitivity and understanding on the part of the physician-diplomat. If a program of medical aid is to be simultaneously a vehicle for a diplomatic effort it must be entrusted to extremely wise physicians who are not only highly competent in their own profession but are also sensitive to the limitations of diplomatic relations and have the courage to bridge the transient but often superficial differences that separate nations.

Not all overseas medical ventures, obviously, are helpful in furthering international understanding. There are painful examples of wasted and misguided effort. During my period of work in Egypt the major clinical research program sponsored by an American unit was on zinc metabolism in Egyptian dwarfs.

Egyptian physicians and politicians alike asked me if that program was selected purposely to offend, since it must have represented the most miniscule health program of that struggling land. How much better it would have been—for medicine, for Egypt, for America—to concern ourselves with the major endemic illnesses of Egypt. Such diseases are rare in our country and difficult to investigate here. We could and should have utilized our unique presence in the very center of a troubled area by identifying ourselves with, for example, the problem of infant diarrhea, which is responsible for over 50 per cent of childhood mortality there. Adjacent to this American research station was a 1,500-bed fever hospital, but when I arrived no cooperative studies had been undertaken there for several years and a rusted lock prevented admission.

With what arrogance did we decide on a study of zinc metabolism which, if it were to be done at all, could be more readily and more effectively accomplished in the sophisticated laboratories of our country? Why should such a research program dominate the only American biochemistry and clinical facilities in an area crying for help against infectious diseases that kill and maim hundreds of thousands annually? In this case a health program not only failed to help international goodwill; it irritated an open wound of misunderstanding and distrust.

In other overseas health projects the physician as well as the bureaucrat must bear the burden for past failures. Medical men have often been unwilling or incapable of *demanding* that the health aspects of developmental projects be considered at every phase of planning and execution. Health must be recognized as integral a part of any human development scheme as are the engineering, economic, or agricultural components. In Africa, several large dam and irrigation projects were completed before the nations became aware—by both human and animal disease and death—of the catastrophic problems produced when the ecology is altered and various vectors of disease are permitted to multiply and spread. This failure of physicians to articulately present their knowledge, arguments, and beliefs in words that are acceptable and understandable to legislators, politicians, and business leaders is no longer tolerable. The men of medicine can no longer abdicate their professional responsibilities nor fail their obligations as citizens of the world.

It is the physicians' code—a good one—to insist that programs dealing with our profession grow from experience and be presented first to our peers. Only then, if proven relevant, should programs be made available for consideration and enactment by the lay public. This program—linking medicine and diplomacy—began, as I have indicated, more than a decade ago while I was working in the Middle East, Africa, and Asia. This concept of combining medicine and diplomacy grew to a conviction that I first presented to a medical audience six years ago, and it then blossomed into a symposium published by the *Bulletin of the New York Academy of Medicine.* The papers presented at that symposium have been edited, and new ones added. I take this opportunity to express my deep gratitude to the professional colleagues who worked with me in the field, and to the editor of the *Bulletin,* Dr. Saul Jarcho, for their assistance.

Having followed the physician's custom of first presenting an idea to one's peers, having allowed the concept to develop over years from intuition to conviction, having secured the interest and following of a highly competent group of leaders in other disciplines, it seems to me time to present this idea as forcefully as possible to the public and in particular to the legislators and leaders who determine or at least enact our foreign policy.

Our nation, and the entire developed world, has paid lip service to the health needs of the vast population in the Third World. Unfortunately, even that lip service has not always been accurate in its premises. Two major reports have recently been issued that, unless corrected, may well serve as a false basis for foreign assistance programs in the 1970's.

The Pearson Report studied many ramifications of foreign aid, and many of its carefully researched studies and conclusions were, I feel, correct and desirable. Its view on health, however, was summarized recently by a group of European medical deans as "almost totally lacking in appreciation of the economic and social significance of public health in global medicine." The report, for example, at one point states that "malaria has been virtually eliminated by a worldwide campaign"—a total inaccuracy about a disease that remains a major medical threat to more than 100 million persons in malarious areas around the world. The World Health Organization has, in fact, recently retreated from its noble but unrealistic goal of worldwide eradication and describes its current aim in the euphemistic phrase "pre-eradication"; i.e., the establishment of basic health facilities and the development of health personnel and programs before again embarking upon specific malaria control.

The Pearson Report also states that the percentage of doctors per population has improved greatly, and notes that in Africa in 1966 the range was 1 to 9,200. As Professor Maegraith of Liverpool responded, "I can only say that in 1969 in one of the better served areas in Nigeria (one of the best in Africa) the ratio was nearer to 1 to 40,000." My own experience in even more destitute areas of Africa and Asia would corroborate that or even a higher ratio.

In this country, the Peterson Report was commissioned by President Nixon in order to determine the future of American foreign assistance in the 1970's. Once again, the report paid loud lip service to health and the eradication of poverty and disease, but no specific health programs were proposed apart from a continuation of the contributions of surplus foods and the humanitarian assistance provided during disasters. New organizations and institutes and councils were suggested, but health was not mentioned as a proposed activity in a single one of them.

It is not only that the Peterson and Pearson reports are wrong on specific points. These could be corrected. There are actually many cogent and imaginative proposals contained in these reports, but the failure to incorporate medicine as an integral component of any proposal intended to fulfill the basic requirements of the Third World is truly lamentable. Lip service will not suffice. The failure to appreciate the diplomatic potential of medicine as a vehicle of international goodwill may well prove a tragedy, if not a continued disaster, for America's foreign policy.

Another myth plaguing international medicine is that easy solution of the unknowing: relegating all global health problems to the World Health Organization. One need only point out that the budget of the New York *City* Health Department is more than ten times that of the entire World Health Organization. The World Health Organization itself makes no pretense of solving the major medical problems around the world, but attempts only to be an advisory and coordinating service. This it does very well, but that hardly meets our need for a new vehicle for international exchanges nor the developing world's need for medical assistance programs at every level.

The marriage of medicine and diplomacy is not without its dangers, as I have pointed out and as several of the contributors in this book will detail. One cannot live without such dangers, but when one considers the dangers inherent in *all* fields of communication between peoples and cultures, medicine, it seems to me, is eminently worth the risk.

Certainly, as shall be presented here, the combination is a realistic goal, it is a feasible one, it is an economically sound one, and, I contend, it will be an inevitable one in the decade ahead.

Few people are as qualified as is the Honorable Angie Brooks to discuss the current and potential role of medicine and diplomacy from the viewpoint of the international organizations. For many years this remarkable woman contributed her leadership to social programs in her native Liberia and in pan-African conferences. Her influence gradually extended around the globe, and in her role as president of the General Assembly of the United Nations (24th Session) she became a forceful embodiment of mankind's struggle for international peace and social progress.

Some of the problems in joining medicine and diplomacy are pointed out by Dr. John Badeau, former ambassador of the United States to the United Arab Republic and currently director of the Middle East Institute at Columbia University. During more than a quarter of a century in the turbulent world of the Middle East Dr. Badeau, as a foundation worker, university president, and finally ambassador, has sought energetically and thought deeply about possible links between nations and how these could be forged into a global chain. Dr. Badeau's thorough review of the philosophic basis for incorporating medicine with diplomacy is completed by a suggestion that we consider the establishment of a completely new administrative channel to permit overseas medical activity to function independent of political change.

Ambassador Abdulrahim Abby Farah of Somalia, a nation on the eastern tip of Africa whose medical needs are poignantly detailed in his contribution, represents the Third World. In his capacity as chairman of the Special Political Committee of the United Nations and as a member of the Security Council, he has the opportunity of traveling extensively throughout the developing lands. His description of medical problems and goals can be applied to many areas outside Somalia.

The economic impact of disease in the Third World and the need to integrate health with all other aspects of a development program are reviewed by Dr. Mark Perlman, University Professor of Economics and Health at the University of Pittsburgh. Dr. Perlman's studies as economist with the Johns Hopkins Health Surveys in Brazil and Taiwan are well known. Among his numerous honors and positions that of editor-in-chief of the *Journal of Economic Literature* partially reflects the esteem in which he is held by his peers.

For the past 25 years, the Most Reverend Edward Swanstrom has been director of the largest American voluntary agency providing overseas aid. The change from merely distributing surplus food to the incorporation of nutritional supplements with self-help programs and with preschool health projects provides one example of medical-diplomatic efforts at a nongovernmental level. Such is the basis of the diplomacy of persuasion.

Dr. George Lythcott's reflections, based on seven years in West Africa both as associate director of the National Institutes of Health program in Ghana and as field director of the highly successful Smallpox Eradication Program, abound with the common sense born of experience, and the call, "if we care," in his peroration is born of hope.

Congressman Hugh L. Carey, a member of the Ways and Means Committee of the House of Representatives, served for more than ten years on the Health, Education, and Welfare panel. As chairman of the subcommittee on Micronesia he has had ample opportunity to examine the health problems in one developing area. His presentation is a clarion call to our government to consider new and practical methods for delivering overseas aid, and he provides specific recommendations as to how this might be done.

It is my fervent hope that the views expressed in this book will provide the basis for planning an alternative approach in foreign aid for the 1970's, and will serve to link nations together through medicine.

Medicine:
Midwife of World Peace

Angie Brooks

S UFFERING EVOKES compassion, and the art of healing which can relieve suffering has been highly regarded from the beginnings of civilized living. When suffering is relieved, a bridge is established between man and man, the eye turns inward and the healer as well as the healed become aware of the ties of human relationship. The religious spirit has found natural expression in the service of the sick and the art of healing has been used as a way to the heart of people separated by language, race, and geography.

Over the centuries the medicine man has worn the mantle of magician, priest, or tribal chief, wielding power by virtue of his specialized knowledge. Physicians have been counsellors and confidants to kings and have served as envoys to foreign lands. With the progress of science and a growing appreciation of the true nature of disease, the art of healing lost its touch of mystery but not its prestige. Indeed, the demonstrated capacity of modern medicine to prevent and cure disease has given it a prestige greater than ever before. The role of medicine—or rather public

11

health, to use a term with a wider connotation—is viewed today in a global context, for the logic of events and the way we live on this shrinking globe have taught us to regard the problem of health and disease in its planetary dimensions.

The most outstanding event of this age is the creation, or rather, the emergence of the United Nations. Notwithstanding the immediate play of forces which brought it into being, the birth of this world body was the culmination of ideas and concepts that had long been shaping in the minds of men—ideas relating to political organization and scientific technology as well as the idealistic impulses and notions of universal love and brotherhood of man, which had found expression in art, religion, and political philosophy.

The ideology which is enshrined in the articles of the Charter, as well as the ideas and practices generated in the course of the work of the UN and its family of specialized agencies, are perhaps the most important contribution of the twentieth century to man's perennial quest—still unattained—for a just social order. In that sense the birth of the UN is not merely a political but also a philosophical event.

Viewed against the backdrop of this new ideology, one gets a new perspective on all major efforts for the well-being of man— in such fields as nutrition, health, education, trade, industry— whether undertaken by a world body, by a regional group of nations, or in a bilateral pattern.

There is, for instance, nothing inherently new in the UN's commitment to the preservation of peace and security as its major goal. But the moment we see it in its full implications it is revealed as a radically revolutionary goal with wide ramifications. For peace in our times is not merely the absence of war but also the creation of conditions in which man everywhere may live in dignity and freedom from want. For peace to be won, there must be waged a constant war on poverty, ill-health, and ignorance.

Thus, we see that man is at the center once again. To enable him to have a better lot, the nations of the world must bend their wills in a concerted effort. And they see this as their task not for altruistic reasons but as a matter of sound common sense and enlightened self-interest. Peace is a vital condition for survival. And peace is impossible in a world ravaged by hunger and disease. To save peace man's basic rights must be guaranteed.

The new ideology is expressed in the preamble to the constitution of the World Health Organization (WHO) in the statement of such principles as the following:

> The enjoyment of the highest attainable standard of health is one of the fundamental rights of every human being without distinction of race, religion, political belief, economic or social condition.

> The health of all peoples is fundamental to the attainment of peace and security and is dependent upon the fullest cooperation of individuals and States.

> The achievement of any State in the promotion and protection of health is of value to all.

> Governments have a responsibility for the health of their peoples which can be fulfilled only by the provision of adequate health and social measures.

The objective of the organization as defined in the constitution, "the attainment by all peoples of the highest possible level of health," is obviously a long-term one, but one can see in it the dedication and confident optimism of today's leaders in medicine and public health.

During the past 22 years, WHO has carried out, in cooperation with its member governments, an extensive program of disease control and health promotion, concentrating always on building up the national health services and helping with the education of all categories of medical and health personnel. From its headquarters in Geneva it conducts a number of technical services which seem inevitably to fall within the jurisdiction of the premier global organization in the health field. These include coordination of a sizable medical research program, including comparative research in cancer, heart disease, and mental health; collection and dissemination of health statistics; an influenza network with 80 centers in 55 countries; international and national reference centers for various diseases and for standardization of vaccines and other biological products; an epidemiological warning service broadcasting daily information on the major contagious diseases. Its most recent international services, to go into operation shortly, include a system for monitoring adverse reactions to drugs and another for air pollution.

The closer one looks at the work of WHO, the threat that disease poses everywhere, and the way it is being met by cooperation among nations and sharing of the latest advances in medical science, make one sharply aware of the common destiny of man and the fact that beneath the patchwork quilt which is the political map of the world, one mankind inhabits the globe. There is little doubt that the worldwide battle for better health cements international bonds and deepens human understanding.

The aim of the effort to promote health under the United Nations system, represented primarily by WHO, is not limited to relieving human suffering, which is, of course, important in itself. It is as part of the global strategy to raise living standards, generally described as development, that international health work can be seen in its true significance for the future of man.

Development involves stimulation of interacting processes in varying fields such as health, education, agriculture, communications, economic growth, trade expansion, and so forth. A common denominator of development work is the introduction of new scientific techniques in a given field. It is reasonable to assume that communities enslaved for generations by such diseases as malaria, bilharziasis, diarrheas, worm infections, and malnutrition, improverished by high mortality rates, and living mostly by subsistence farming under a constant burden of sickness, will neither have the will nor the capacity to absorb and try out new ideas in, say, farming techniques or children's education.

The physician, with his capacity to relieve suffering and to answer an immediately felt need, has greater possibility of being accepted by a community. He is then able to set up a bridgehead from which the multipronged development battle can effectively be launched. Health effort in such a community must be appreciated also in terms of conserving and building up the major, sometimes the only, resource—the human resource. Development efforts can hardly take root in a disease-ridden community, where the only source of energy is muscle power.

Thus we see that the physician, like his predecessors, continues to enjoy his unique privilege of being accepted in the heart of the family and community. He goes about his task today not as a lone individual but as a member of both a health team and a multidisciplinary force whose goal is wider than taking care of the sick.

His new role is in keeping with the modern concept of health which is defined in the WHO constitution as not merely the absense of disease but "a state of complete physical, mental, and social well-being."

Medicine, with other branches of knowledge, has joined battle today in the only war that is worth fighting. Its aim is to break the grip of the vicious cycle of disease-breeding poverty and poverty-breeding disease, in an unending process. A lasting peace will be possible only when the word becomes meaningful for those millions of people in our world whose very existence is no more than a daily battle to keep alive.

Diplomacy and Medicine

John S. Badeau

T O PLACE MEDICINE and diplomacy in the same equation is neither new nor novel. The diplomatic records of ancient Egypt tell us that about 29 centuries ago the famous physician-priests of the Nile Valley sometimes accompanied Egyptian missions to neighboring countries and acted as ambassadors. We find that millennia later during the Crusades, Arab doctors played a part in the contacts between Saladin and his Frankish opponents. On more than one occasion the Christian leaders appealed to their Arab foe for Muslim physicians, whose skill was superior to anything Europe then knew. Contemporary accounts from this period do not record a high level of medical skill on the part of the Frankish practitioners. One Arab doctor tells of being called to treat the ulcerous leg of a Christian knight—which he did with unguents and poultices. The Christian doctor who watched the process was then invited to give his prescription. This consisted of having the camp executioner chop off the affected limb since, said the Frank, "Cases like this are hopeless and I don't know how to cure them."

This ancient, although incidental, connection between medicine and diplomacy reflects the fact that health (even more than wealth) is a common and prized good. Political allies sought not only financial and military assistance from their neighbors but also the services of healing when these were available. Moreover, medicine has been one of the first professions to emerge in a society; hence doctors were an early part of the emerging intellectual elite. It was natural that some of them should be called upon to serve their governments in capacities other than that of their profession. I was interested to note that during my term at the American embassy in Cairo, the diplomatic corps had a number of doctors in it—including some from African and South American countries.

It is not this ancient and simple connection between the doctor and the diplomat which concerns us. The question is more complex: do current international relations offer a special challenge to medical and health services? We are really asking whether there is a *new diplomacy* which creates a new role for the medical profession—or whether there may be a new profession of health care which has a unique contribution to make to current diplomacy.

In what sense is there a new diplomacy today? If we go back to the classical age of foreign affairs (roughly from the Congress of Vienna to the end of World War I) we find that diplomacy was a limited operation carried on under generally accepted rules by recognized professionals. It was said that foreign policy was like an orchestra—a harmony produced by the interchange of notes among highly skilled professional artists. This meant that the conduct of foreign affairs was in the hands of the restricted group that staffed the foreign offices of the world. It was among this corps of professional diplomats that most of the discussions of international politics went on, usually behind the closed doors of Foreign Offices. Thus at the Congress of Vienna the professional diplomats of Europe met for an extended discussion on the problems created by the collapse of Napoleon's empire, to emerge finally from their seclusion with a series of agreements which set the pattern of international relations in Europe for the next 50 years.

This state of affairs began to change shortly after World War I. A number of elements then entered the world scene which made it inevitable that diplomacy should take on new characteristics. One of these was the rapid expansion of public communication through the cable, press and, later, radio and television. The rapid and wide dissemination of news about national and international affairs made it increasingly difficult for the professional diplomats to treat foreign affairs as their special preserve with the masses excluded from it. Increasingly the public became aware of, and thus interested in, national policies both domestic and foreign. Incidents between nations, which in the past would have been quietly and quickly worked out between diplomats before they became public knowledge, now became the immediate possession of all who could read or tune in on the airwaves. One British administrator in Africa told me how this had complicated the task of diplomacy. "Before the war," he said, "when there was a border incident I would get in touch with my opposite number in the neighboring territory and we quickly worked out a solution. Only after the matter was settled did it become public knowledge. Today the most insignificant border incident is on the radio almost before it happens. By the time I get in touch with the other chap it has become a matter of national honor and patriotic dignity, from which it is difficult to find any retreat."

To the impact of widely disseminated information has been added the effects of nationalism and popular education. Decades of struggle for national independence in colonial areas taught the masses that they had a role to play in their nation's life. During the protracted campaigns for independence, crowds were organized for street demonstrations, students for protest and rioting, and every citizen was urged to support "national liberation." A voiceless and politically inert class, seldom before called upon to play a role in national affairs, suddenly discovered that it had a place in them. Having been awakened to this fact during the struggle for independence, this class was unwilling to lapse into passivity once independence had been gained.

This popularization of political concern was aided by the spread of education. Traditionally the educated elite in colonial and undeveloped areas was only a minute fraction of the population. The common man had neither the opportunity nor the expectation of going to school. But with the founding of national systems of education and the resulting rapid proliferation of schools, many more people are being educated than ever before. Figures vary from country to country but, as an example, about 80 per cent of the children of primary-school age now attend school in the United Arab Republic; 20 years ago less than one third of them did so. The increase is not only absolute in terms of the number of pupils, it is also relative to the classes of society who are being educated. A different kind of person is going to school today in many emerging countries—the peasant, the laborer, the urban poor, some tribesmen—all of them typical of that elusive but ubiquitous "common man" who is the foundation of all society. Whatever the education given in school, its invariable effect is to broaden the horizons of the students and their families; this breaks down their isolation from national affairs and makes them feel they have entered the class of educated people who traditionally have guided the affairs of the nation.

As a result of these factors, diplomacy and the foreign policy with which it deals has been given a new audience which it addresses and to which it must listen. The day when a small intellectual elite could settle the foreign policy of a country and negotiate diplomatic relations through a professional corps without reference to popular opinion is gone. In every country there is now a public opinion which must be taken into account by the diplomat. This is as true in emerging countries under authoritarian rule as in more democratic societies. Foreign affairs can no longer be the preserve of the professional; they now include the dimension of popular interest and opinion.

This is illustrated clearly by the impact of the war in Vietnam on the conduct of American foreign policy. The United States has participated in other wars to which objections could be raised; the most recent was the Korean war which began in 1950. Why has there been so much more outcry over Vietnam? I believe it is largely because of the constant flow of radio news bulletins, the television reporting which brings the sights and sounds of war into the living room every night, and a generation of students who have been awakened to international affairs. It may be true, as Senator Hugh Scott said, that foreign policy cannot be made by the crowds in the streets and the byways, but obviously it is impossible for any administration to frame a policy on Vietnam without taking into account what is being said in the streets and byways.

Another new factor affecting the conduct of diplomacy arises from the same ease of communication which generates popular participation in national affairs. It is now possible for a chief of state to speak about foreign affairs not only to his own citizens but also to the citizens of other countries. President Richard M. Nixon on television or President Gamal Abdel Nasser in Liberation Square in Cairo could go over the heads of their own foreign officers and diplomatic corps to present policies to popular audiences and to appeal for their support. This not only increases the consciousness of the citizenry of their political role, it may also affect popular opinion in another country with which a diplomatic problem exists. There can be no doubt that part of North Vietnam's diplomacy has been to seek direct appeals to the American public for the purpose of arousing opinion in the United States against the policies of the American government. Similarly, statements by American leaders, some broadcast throughout the nation over television and some relayed abroad by satellite, are aimed at influencing public attitudes outside as well as within American borders. Diplomacy is thus no longer a matter of diplomats talking to diplomats; it often involves governments talking over the heads of their diplomats to the citizens of other countries in the hope of affecting their attitudes.

Since World War II, the conduct of diplomacy has been profoundly affected by the emergence of an unprecedented number of new, if small, nations. The future historian may well conclude that the most significant feature of these past decades has not been the emergence of atomic power, but the emergence into political freedom of a large segment of the world's population. Since the ending of World War II, more than one billion people in some thirty countries have passed from foreign control to independence and sovereignty. Diplomacy today does not operate in a world composed of a few great powers around whom cluster colonies, protectorates, mandates, and spheres of interest. It must function amidst a multicentric system of political power where a majority of the nations are small states—many of them new—and where all claim the full prerogatives of their sovereignty.

Out of this situation has grown a new dimension of diplomatic activity that concerns the economic and social development of emerging states. In the past, people struggling for independence often appealed to world powers on the grounds that political freedom is an inherent human right and that the great powers had a responsibility for ensuring that this right was given to all who sought it. Thus during the Algerian struggle in the 1950's, the Algerian independence movement despatched emissaries to foreign governments, including the United States, to urge that the world community owed them political freedom. This view is still widely held, but most newly independent nations have now added to it a further demand: the right to economic and social growth. Emerging nations discovered that political independence did not, as expected, solve all their problems. It was not enough to be free; it was also necessary to be progressive and prosperous. As the world owed them a debt of political freedom, so, these nations maintained, it owed a debt of economic and technical assistance.

Thus the diplomacy of the postwar period has had to respond to new demands. Even though a particular economic situation might not vitally affect the immediate interest of a great power, it was often impossible to pursue political ends without meeting some of the economic demands of the recipient country.

But it was not merely pressure from developing countries which added this dimension to postwar diplomacy. Stability, economic growth, and progress in developing areas were quickly recognized by some great powers as favorable to their own interests. Poverty, backwardness, and unfulfilled expectations could easily create both political and economic instability and set off clashes which might well imperil the peace of the world. Thus one of the two major global objectives of the United States after World War II was to support in vital areas the forces which made for political and social stability, so that the danger of "brush-fire" wars would be reduced and external radical forces would not be tempted to exacerbate domestic conflicts.

One final factor in postwar diplomacy must be noted. Although the war resulted in the emergence of two superpowers, the United States and the Soviet Union, neither of these has retained the capacity to have its way absolutely in world affairs. It might be thought that the vast armaments and political prestige of either country would make possible the enforcement of almost any foreign policy it desired. Yet this has not proved to be the case. The proliferation of independent states with the status in world affairs given them by membership in the United Nations has circumscribed the direct influence of the great powers. It was not difficult for a major power to control and direct the policies of its colonies, protectorates, spheres of influence, and clients in the old imperial days; but today these same areas, now fiercely independent and proudly sovereign, do not easily come to heel. The very extent of military force available to either superpower has militated against its use for diplomatic ends. The continued balance of terror between the Western and the Communist blocs is such that neither side can use its weapons to maintain diplomatic pressure on other nations. Both the East European clients of the U.S.S.R. and America's partners in Europe and Asia have been able to pursue freer foreign policies because of this situation.

This means that diplomacy today must more often use a diplomacy of persuasion rather than a diplomacy of pressure. Both American and Soviet attempts to order their alleged clients

around have not proved very successful, as the continued stale-
mate between Israel and some of the Arab states clearly shows.
Unless a diplomatic problem affects its most vital national interests, a great power must depend upon its ability to persuade
another power to accept a mutually satisfactory course of action.
This means that common interests and shared objectives become
central to diplomatic practice.

From this brief description emerges the picture of a new diplomacy closely related to the popular mind in emerging countries,
based upon shared interests and expressing itself in economic and
technical as well as in political terms. Foreign aid and technical
assistance have become a large part of foreign policy in the postwar years. Subsidies, grants, loans, and limited technical services
have long played a role in the relations betwen nations, but never
before have there been such comprehensive, massive, and sustained programs of aid as during the past two decades. Beginning
with the Marshall Plan, Western and Communist nations alike
have made foreign aid a substantial and vital part of their policies.
In some relations between countries these programs have been
the major instrument of diplomacy; they may account for the
largest expenditure of funds, the most numerous personnel, and
the most frequent contacts with the host governments.

It is at once obvious that in this field of diplomacy—i.e., technical and developmental aid—services of health and healing
have an opportunity to play a significant role. Every emerging
country is challenged by its own independence to provide better
health for its citizens. One of the first steps of modernization is
usually the establishment of government-directed health services,
in the fields of preventive and curative medicine. The demand for
such services comes not only from the government but also from
the common people. Go into even the most remote villages of the
Middle East and ask: "What do you want?" and the answer
usually will be: "A doctor and a school."

This being true, health programs would seem to meet some of
the needs of the new diplomacy in almost ideal fashion. Since

health is desired and readily understood by the common man, any foreign contribution to public health would immediately be recognized as valuable by the recipient. Long-range technical programs of development may be essential for building the economic strength of a new country, but often they take years to mature and are not quickly identified by those they are designed to serve.

Moreover, health is one of the basic, universal human interests—the kind of "shared concern" for which the diplomat is often searching. The utility of and the need for health does not require argument either in a giving or a receiving country, and contributions of assistance in the health field are immediately apprehended and eagerly sought. One sign of this is the fact that in the United Arab Republic the Naval Medical Research Unit (NAMRU) was quickly reestablished after the Six Day War and is operating today—even though political and diplomatic relations between Egypt and the United States remain broken.

But the contribution of medicine and health is not simply one of charity and compassion, represented at its best by the missionary hospital and doctor who have contributed so much to the emerging world. New governments and emerging countries want to establish their own health services, and the problem is how to render assistance in this field with the primary objective of developing the capability of the receiving government to operate its own health program. It is comparatively simple for a foreign doctor to go into another country, open a clinic or hospital, and personally attack the problems of ill-health and disease. It is much more difficult and complicated to refrain from doing this in the interest of helping national doctors, hospitals, and clinics to perform the work. Yet this is the goal of true technical and medical assistance.

It might be concluded from all this that every embassy ought to have a medical staff attached to it and that every American aid program should include a technical-assistance team working in the field of public health. Yet this is highly questionable. Although the contribution of health obviously is important and useful, it is a particularly difficult one to make within the limitations of a diplomatic mission.

There are several reasons for this. One is that programs of assistance closely tied to diplomacy cannot escape the pressures of political objectives. Congress does not make appropriations for programs of aid out of the goodness of its heart—or as one Congressman put it—"United States aid programs are not meant to play Santa Claus." While there is a genuine interest in economic and social development, appropriations are scrutinized increasingly by legislators with a view to winning host governments to the acceptance of American policy.

The use of aid for political ends is always resented by those who receive it, but it is particularly resented when that aid deals with such basic human needs as food and health. Our experience with the Food for Peace program in the United Arab Republic was that any alteration in that program which appeared to be dictated by political ends brought an immediate outcry from Egyptians: "You are using the threat of starvation to coerce us." This is equally true in the field of health. Given current attitudes in Congress and the virtual certainty that aid programs will expand or contract in proportion to their success in securing support for the United States, to tie the services of health closely to the diplomatic mission might be disastrous.

Former Undersecretary of State Nicholas deB. Katzenbach recognized this when he said: "Aid can be a liability as well as an asset to bilateral relations. These countries strongly resent the use of aid for purposes they consider extraneous to the aid relationship; namely, as a lever to compel conformity to our foreign policy."

How, then, can health services be used in the relations between two countries, yet remain insulated from the impact of political diplomacy? In some cases, where we are working with allies with whom we have few political problems, it is possible to place health programs under the general direction of aid operations. Yet often such programs are in areas which need services least. I suggest that what is needed is a more complete separation between that assistance which deals with basic human needs—health, education, and food—and other types of economic and technical assistance. This could be accomplished best by a private professional organization, responsible for furthering health programs abroad, yet financed in large measure by grants from the United States Government.

An example of this type of administration (rare in the United States) is the British Council, which has played an important role in bringing British culture to emerging nations. The British Council is financed by grants from Parliament, but is itself a nongovernmental agency conducted by professional specialists who are responsible for defining and conducting its program. While the Council represents British influence and serves the general cause of Anglo-foreign understanding, it has been remarkably free from the accusation of serving immediate political or diplomatic ends.

I suggest that the contributions of medicine to the needs of developing countries could best be made under some such form as the British Council. The initial leadership would have to come from the ranks of the medical and health professions rather than from the United States Government, but a sustained concern for the formation of a private organization seeking government support might succeed. Some private American universities abroad have received government funds, especially from counterpart monies, and it is not impossible that health programs cast in a similar relation could win support. Certainly we should not allow either the current temper of Congress or the difficulties in depoliticizing aid programs to deter us from pressing for a larger role for medicine in the relations of the United States with other countries.

In the last analysis, the success of the affluent Western world in dealing with the emerging areas will not be determined by military might or diplomatic pressure. It will come from the success of the developed countries in identifying themselves with the urgent problems of new nations by contributing to their solutions. This is true of the Soviet-American rivalry in the Middle East as well as elsewhere. Surely we must press for a new and imaginative approach to the use of health services as we seek this long-range goal.

Health Problems and Goals
of a Developing Nation

Abdulrahim Abby Farah

M ANY AFRICAN STATES today are in the midst of a process
of transformation as traditional ways of living meet the challenges
involved in contact with technologically advanced societies. If it
were desirable to ignore this challenge, the radio, jet plane, and
television have made it impossible to do so. The emergence of
African states to political independence itself demands, as they
take their places in the family of nations, that they embark on a
course of modernization aimed at reducing, as rapidly as possible,
the economic inequality of their societies vis-à-vis those societies
where technological and scientific knowledge have ensured a
higher standard of living.

It is right that people in Africa, as elsewhere, should want to
achieve material progress, but tremendous problems have been
created by increasing demands from expanding populations for
better services, more educational facilities, and more opportunities for jobs. Since many of the developing countries are poor—
either because their resources have not yet been fully developed

or because they have few natural resources—governments have to make agonizing decisions when they try to assign priorities for the long list of developmental needs. It is against this general background that the health problems and goals of a developing nation such as my own—the Somali Democratic Republic—must be viewed.

Somalia's basic health needs are similar to those of the majority of the developing countries of Africa. First, we have most of the diseases that beset other countries as well as some which apply particularly to Africa: we need, for example, campaigns both for tuberculosis control and for the eradication of smallpox; second, we suffer from an acute shortage of doctors, nurses, and other medical personnel; third, we need assistance in the form of financial, material, or technical aid, in order to carry out the services that are necessary for maintaining good standards of health including additional hospitals and laboratories; fourth, we need to plan very carefully to ensure that the best use is made of our financial resources and that health programs will be suited to the needs of a predominantly nomadic population which adheres strongly to its cultural traditions.

A look at some of the health programs in Somalia will pinpoint our most obvious problems of disease.

A World Health Organization (WHO) malaria pre-eradication campaign aims, in the words of that organization, "to build up the technical, administrative, and operational facilities for a full-scale malaria eradication program and, at the same time, to develop the rural health services, so that they may provide efficient collaboration in the eradication program."[1] An example of the kind of information that such preliminary surveys elicit is the discovery that the use of medicated salt—successful among the Iranian nomads—is not feasible in Somalia since the nomad herdsmen consume almost no salt.[2] Mass drug distribution has not been found to be a satisfactory approach to the eradication of malaria either, as Somali nomads scatter during the malaria transmission season. Spraying operations were carried out successfully in urban areas, but particular problems were encountered when these were applied to the nomads. In the northern region of the country, an attempt to spray caravans moving to and returning from "wet" grazing areas met with little success because of the impossible task of keeping track of thousands of caravans moving over widely scattered areas and because of insufficient propagation of the scheme and the consequent lack of cooperation from the people.

Tuberculosis is, perhaps, our biggest health program. The United Nations International Children's Emergency Fund (UNICEF) is carrying out a tuberculosis-control program to test, in certain areas, a simple, practical, and effective method of preventing and treating tuberculosis, including vaccination and the examination of sputum.[3] Under this program a number of health centers have been set up to offer preventive and curative services. Dealing mainly with mothers and their children, they are also used as training centers for personnel. WHO is working on a program for the eradication of smallpox and a survey of yellow fever.[4]

Dr. Kevin M. Cahill, the editor of this book, has done extremely valuable work in tracing the incidence of various types of diarrheal diseases in Somalia.[5] The importance of this research is underlined by the fact that such diseases account for more deaths in the "under-four" age group than any other single cause.[6]

As far as our goal to increase the supply of doctors and other medical assistants is concerned there are two important needs that have to be considered in planning for the training of medical personnel for a country like Somalia. The experience of other African countries has shown the need for a special curriculum for our students who study medicine abroad. African students are usually trained in the European tradition and it is often difficult for some of them to adjust to the fact that medicine in Africa cannot be practiced in the consulting room or operating theater alone, but must be related to the social and community aspects of disease.

The other consideration is that recognition must be given to the special role played by local medical assistants in the total picture of medical services. In Somalia, these workers—usually males—have risen from the ranks through the level of the dresser and, because of particular economic and social conditions, have played and should continue to play a very important part in our health programs. Most of them are skilled and highly intelligent persons; they lack all but the academic background necessary for professional training and are able to perform a great part of the more routine work of doctors. Since doctors are in short supply it is extremely useful to have a cadre of assistants whose work ensures that the best use will be made of the professional talents of fully trained doctors. Our government, in consultation with WHO and UNICEF, has given priority to the training of such people, and a Health Institute has been set up and will instruct various categories of auxiliary personnel.

With regard to the third factor on my list of basic health needs: namely, assistance in the form of financial, material, and technical aid, successive Somali governments have welcomed and continue to welcome aid from many different countries. As a nonaligned nation we accept such offers on their merits and quite apart from any political considerations. May I add here the assurance that a change of government, in our country or in any other, does not signify any change in the health needs and goals of the nation which, after all, remain the same, whatever government is in power.

The question of the financial and other resources available for health programs is closely bound up with our fourth basic need: careful planning to ensure the best use of these resources. Planning for health must take several factors into account. First, priorities must be established between health and other developmental programs aimed at educating the population and raising the standard of living. Then, priorities for different types of health programs must be ranked. Next, the implications of health programs which are to be introduced must be studied carefully.

The difficulty of assigning priorities between different developmental schemes becomes immediately apparent if one agrees that a sound medical program can be established only on the basis of progress in the field of education and, more fundamentally, on the basis of general economic progress. Raising the standard of education in general is a necessary step toward achieving goals for health, but attempts to educate the people will be of no avail if the standard of living is not improved. Dr. H. B. L. Russell, WHO liaison officer with the Economic Commission for Africa, posed the problem in this way: "No amount of talking and lecturing will persuade people on a very low economic level to adopt measures for which their social situation does not make the need clear: as the standard of living rises, so does the call for better sanitation and housing and improvements in the environment."[7]

What, then, is the prospect for improving the standard of living in Somalia so that benefits such as a general improvement of the health of the population may occur? The economy of the country is fundamentally a subsistence economy. Of the estimated 246,-000 square miles which comprise the territory, approximately 20 per cent can be used for agricultural purposes and about 60 per cent for grazing; the remainder is barren. More than 70 per cent of the population are nomadic herdsmen whose lives are spent with their flocks of sheep, camels, or goats in an unrelenting search for grazing and water.

The life of the nomad is supported by his animals, which provide him with milk, meat, and transport. The sale of sheep and goat skins to local traders provides him with the simple necessities of life, and the export of the skins as the raw material for fine kid leather provides a long-established export trade. This trade has declined somewhat of late because of the introduction of synthetic leather. However, there is also a lively export trade in camels, sheep, and goats on the hoof, particularly to the Middle Eastern countries.

Agriculture, carried on in the south between the two permanent rivers—the Juba and the Webi Shabele—provides the country's most profitable export: bananas. Attempts are being made to diversify agriculture and to make a country which formerly im-

ported all its food except meat and milk self-sufficient in staples
such as grain, sugar, and rice.

Prospecting for oil has been carried on for several years without result, but an exciting development has been the discovery of
uranium after a United Nations survey of mineral resources. Con-
cessions have been given to United States, Italian, and West Ger-
man companies, and these firms are attempting to ascertain if
mining the deposits is economically worthwhile.

One of the great drawbacks to economic, social, and health
programs in Somalia is the shortage of water in our largely semiarid country. Every few years we have to declare certain areas as
famine areas because of drought. There are two permanent rivers
in the southernmost region of the country but elsewhere the
people depend on boreholes, wells, and water pans for their water
supply. Many of the wells and water pans become exhausted
during the dry season and the consequent lack of water presents
a real threat to life. When the seasonal rains fail, as they do peri-
odically in many areas, the perennial problem takes on the pro-
portions of a disaster. In 1969, for example, an emergency situation necessitating international relief was declared in substantial
areas of the northeastern part of Somalia, where over 200,000
nomads were affected.

Scarcity is not the only problem connected with water supplies
in Somalia. Even utilizing the river waters for development purposes presents a hazard—that of the spread of parasitic infections, in particular schistosomiasis, a serious disease transmitted
in the canals and sewers of my nation. A Food and Agriculture
Organization (FAO) project to design irrigation schemes in the
Shabele River Valley has been provided by the World Health
Organization (WHO) with a team composed of an epidemiologist
and a sanitary engineer whose task is to assess the health hazards
of the project.

In addition, there is the problem presented by the absence of
environmental sanitation and the ignorance of precautionary
health measures; this means that often the water available is not
safe to drink.

This is a very brief outline of our resources but it should be sufficient to show that only with a great deal of external assistance —both financial and technical—can the necessary infrastructure for economic development be established and sustained. Assistance is presently being received from the European Economic Community (EEC), of which we are an associate member, and from a number of countries, but the needs and the problems are monumental. Take the question of developing our agricultural resources. Even if the technical personnel and capital were available for irrigation schemes (extremely costly ventures in a country which is mainly semiarid), there would still be the difficulty of persuading the proud nomad, who looks with disdain on the agriculturalist, to settle down and practice farming.

It is clear that for the foreseeable future the main pattern of life for a large proportion of the population will be that of the nomadic pastoralist, and high priority must be given to development plans aimed at making his lot easier. These plans are mainly centered around the provision of more water for the nomad and his animals through the drilling of boreholes and providing treatment for animal diseases. Such treatment will make his livestock more useful to him and more suitable for export—on the hoof and in the form of skins. The animals will also be more suitable for use in the small but growing meat-canning industry.

High priority must also be given to the difficult task of educating the nation. In Somalia this task is complicated by the fact that few settled communities exist outside the main towns. It has been estimated that 2,000,000 Somalis are on the move over this part of Africa at any given time. Providing education and other services for a largely illiterate and predominantly nomadic population is a tremendous task; it calls not only for large-scale financing but also for new approaches to deal with our particular educational problems. An approach now underway is that of giving short intensive courses to the traditional holy men or *widads* who have always traveled with nomadic communities in order to teach the Koran to the young boys of the tribe. The *widads* now teach the children to read, write and calculate, and give them some knowledge of the outside world and Somalia's relation to it. They also give talks to adults and children on land conservation, first aid, and hygiene.

But unless a boy has relatives with whom he can stay in a town where there is a school, his formal education ends with the *widads'* limited store of knowledge. With the help of the United Nations Educational, Scientific, and Cultural Organization (UNESCO), surveys have been made and plans formulated for providing more educational facilities in settled communities, and for boarding schools in interior areas where nomads congregate seasonally. But a few statistics will show how far we have to go before we can arrive at an educational standard comparable to that of more advanced countries. For an estimated population of approximately 3.5 million, the enrollment of children in elementary schools is approximately 30,000; in intermediate schools, 12,000, and about 3,000 in secondary schools. Just over 1,000 Somalis are pursuing degree courses overseas.[8]

The problem of education in general—and of education in health also—is compounded by the language difficulty. The Somali Democratic Republic is composed of the former British Somaliland and the former Trusteeship Territory of Somali administered by Italy. When it acquired independence, the country had three official languages: Arabic, English, and Italian. The common tongue—Somali—has never been written, since the question of whether it should be written in Arabic, in Roman, or in a locally devised script known as Osmania has long been a subject of contention between philologists and politicians. So children begin to learn Arabic at the elementary level; then English or Italian is added at the intermediate level.

The fact that Somali is not written means that it is extremely difficult for government authorities to give even simple instructions—for example, on hygiene or agricultural methods—to the majority of the population. Our new government has promised that it will address itself promptly to the task of creating a written script for the Somali language and it is to be hoped that this great need will soon be filled.

A very useful method of communicating is by radio. In recent years Somalia has made increased use of its broadcasting services to reach the nomads. The ubiquitous transistor radio is an ideal receiver for this purpose and has found its way into some of the nomadic hamlets. Unfortunately it is beyond the means of the majority of the people. If it were economically possible to make transistor radios available to a larger proportion of the nomadic population, this would be an important contribution to the problem of adult education.

I have dealt at some length with Somalia's economic and educational problems because obviously our health needs and goals can best be seen in relation to those problems. I have already said that in establishing priorities one must rank health needs with economic and social requirements and that one must also choose between various health programs. It must be decided, for example, whether increased provision of medical treatment is more important than an intensive program of preventive health education. Obviously there should be provision for both, but if funds are limited, it must be decided if the greater proportion of the resources available should be put into one area, or whether modest advances should be made in a number of directions.

Overall planning for Somalia's health services is being done with the advice and technical assistance of WHO. Modest programs have been initiated with the aim of providing the most basic health requirements of each area rather than emphasizing any one area. I have already mentioned the Health Training Institute for auxiliary personnel. In addition, the nursing services are being strengthened by an improvement in the program for education in nursing. Improved services in surgery and anesthesiology are being provided and a public-health laboratory is being established. An important project planned for the area of public health is the setting up of a rural demonstration and training pro-

gram that will provide practical training and experience in the
development of an integrated public-health service in a rural area.

The difficulty of deciding on medical priorities in Somalia can
be illustrated by the fact that there are only 96 doctors—mostly
attached to hospitals—serving the entire population of three to
four million people at the present time. These figures point to a
need for more doctors and more facilities for medical care.
Mobile units that could help to extend medical services of various
kinds to the nomads on the move would be an obvious benefit.
But there is perhaps an even greater need for extensive programs
of preventive medicine and health education in a country where
ignorance, suspicion of the methods and ideas of the outside
world, and the strong prejudices of a proud and individualistic
people militate against progress.[9]

I have already mentioned that the nomad looks with scorn on
farming and farmers. There are many other things which he views
with contempt: fishermen and fish, for example. A Somali family
might prefer to go without sufficient food and suffer the consequences of malnutrition rather than take advantage of the vast,
mainly untapped source of protein that lies in the waters of the
longest national coastline in Africa. In a land where malnutrition,
especially among children, is common during the frequent periods
of drought it is ironic that eating habits exclude many nutrition-
ally valuable foods.

That a variety of factors must often be taken into consideration
when plans are being made to launch a campaign for health was
vividly illustrated in 1943 when the colonial medical authorities
attempted to introduce a campaign for vaccination in what was
then the Somaliland Protectorate. Political unrest, together with
the normal suspicion of foreign motives and methods, led to the
spreading of a rumor that the vaccinations were meant to make
Somali women sterile. In one of the main townships there were
serious riots in opposition to the campaign and many people were
seriously injured.

Once the process of modernization has been set in motion there are inevitable clashes with the forces of tradition. The main hospital in Hargeisa once had to be closed down temporarily because the European medical superintendent—an otherwise well-qualified man but sadly deficient in his knowledge of Somali customs—ordered the local hospital staff to give bedpans to patients. He was unaware that social custom had apportioned jobs of that nature to a particular clan and that it was *infra dig* for other clans to undertake such tasks. This happened 20 years ago and, fortunately, incidents of that kind are less likely to occur now that Somalis have replaced foreigners in positions of authority. But, generally speaking, social customs and local prejudices must be taken into account in the formulation of development plans.

Somalis possess a considerable body of native medical practice, and while certain practices and principles are not without value, many of them hinder the acceptance of modern medicine. It is interesting to note that Sir Richard Burton reported, in a footnote to his account of his travels in East Africa in the 1850's, that the Somalis believe that malaria is transmitted by mosquitoes. He added that they held this "superstition" because mosquitoes and malarial fevers both appeared at sundown.[10] The principle, at least, behind modern malaria eradication comes as no surprise to Somalis. They have also long been aware of the gravity of tuberculosis and of its contagious nature. Persons suffering from this disease have always been housed separately and, before the advent of modern methods of treatment, they were always given the salutation "God have mercy on you" instead of the more customary "may God restore your health"—a reflection of the realization that nothing could be done for the victim. Many Somalis, too, are expert bonesetters and surgeons and can perform tonsillectomies and trepanning operations.

By and large, however, Somali medicine is reminiscent of medieval medicine. Bloodletting is considered valuable for many ailments; it is carried out in such painful ways as cutting the veins under the tongue and under the eyelids or by drawing off blood in affected areas of the body through small incisions. While the

Somali belief that fire and disease cannot exist together is somewhat compatible with a knowledge of bacteriology, the practice
of branding areas of the body in certain traditional patterns in
order to cure a variety of illnesses ranging from tetanus to appen-
dicitis is one that certainly requires reassessment.

It is clearly important for psychological and practical reasons
to take into account local beliefs and practices. In medicine, as in
other fields, traditions that are valuable can best be preserved by
incorporating them into the mainstream of scientific and technological progress. Certainly education for health must aim at re-
placing widespread reliance on questionable or outmoded practices with respect for modern medical procedures.

This process is already well established and people are becoming increasingly aware of the efficacy of modern methods of treatment. The statistics on the treatment of hernia are significant in
this regard. Until recently, nomads who developed inguinal hernia
became the object of derision and social ostracism. The nature
and cause of the condition was not known to Somali traditional
medicine, and no cure could be advanced for its treatment. It was
generally attributed to malformation, and sufferers were considered to be sexually impotent.

The condition, because of its limitations on the movement of
sufferers, affected adversely the contribution which they could
make to the community and consequently their status and stand-
ing. The life of the nomad is by no means easy, even for the fit
ones. For those who are physically infirm, the odds against their
survival are high. Apart from the physical pain, the sufferers had
also to contend with the derision caused by the somewhat comical
postures which sufferers had to adopt when they walked in order
to relieve pain and pressure on the sensitive parts of their organ,
and by embarrassing noises from the intestines which often accompanied movement. This writer can recall a case where the
sufferer committed suicide rather than face the social unpleasant-
ness which public knowledge of his obvious condition would

bring. But today operations for all types of hernias are among the main surgical problems that are dealt with in the large hospitals. Of greater significance is the fact that the condition is now understood and is no longer a cause for social ostracism.

There was a time when it was difficult to persuade people to come to a hospital for medical treatment. Now, the supply of medical services cannot keep up with the demand. Hospital beds are always occupied and there are always long waiting lists. This new attitude is, of course, a healthy one, but it has created its own problems. It has been difficult for new developments to keep pace with needs that are being recognized for the first time, the chief difficulty being that the whole financial burden of medical care has to be borne by public facilities. There are at most nine or ten doctors in private practice in the whole country and most of the people are too poor in any case to pay for medical care or drugs.

It might seem that taking the traditional culture of a people into account when planning health projects for developing countries would make the process complicated enough, but there are other social, economic, and health implications which need careful study. For example, it has been found in some countries that a successful program for eradicating malaria has resulted in the survival of a large number of infants and children who formerly would have died from malaria or allied causes. This is not to say that such programs should not be carried out for this reason. But it does mean that additional facilities in services such as education, and later in job opportunities, have to be provided and planning should take account of this.

It is pertinent to emphasize here the need for foreign governments and international organizations that offer assistance to developing African nations to pay particular attention to the special conditions prevailing in each recipient country, and to orient their approaches accordingly. There is as great diversity in Africa as in South America, and it would be imprudent to expect that a medical program applied successfully in one country would automatically succeed in another, even though the countries concerned might be neighbours.

However, there are certain basic factors common to all developing countries which must be taken into account in assessing the needs of any one country. These factors are the interrelated ones of illiteracy, ignorance, and poverty. One of the results of illiteracy is, of course, a shortage of trained local people. Ignorance gives rise to problems in the communication of new ideas and attitudes. Poverty on the family level means a low standard of living which itself inhibits the desire for self-improvement; on the national level it demands the most rigorous examination of priorities and the seemingly impossible task of choosing between programs all of which appear to be equally necessary.

I think I have presented enough to show that the Somali Democratic Republic is faced with a complex pattern of interlinked problems. But progress, however small, is being made in every area. Our new government is particularly aware of the deficiencies of the program for health and is determined to end the stagnation caused in the past by inefficient organization and the maladministration of resources.

Specialized agencies of the United Nations—WHO, UNICEF, and FAO—are giving invaluable technical and material assistance. In addition, the Republic has benefitted from the services of medical teams, medical equipment, and medicine provided by many governments, including those of the Soviet Union, Italy, China, the United Arab Republic, West Germany, and the United States. If our problems are large, so is the goodwill that continues to be shown toward our country and the energies of our government and people that are being used toward their solution.

Notes

1. UN Document EM/RC 19/2, p. 170.
2. J. Simon, *Men and Medicine in the Middle East,* WHO Regional Office for the Eastern Mediterranean, 1967.
3. UN Document EM/RC 19/2, p. 170.
4. *Ibid.,* pp. 172-175.
5. K. Cahill, I. Davies, and R. Johnson, "Report of an Epidemic due to *Shigella Dysenteriae," American Journal of Tropical Medicine and Hygiene* 15 (1966) 52.
6. J. Simon, *op. cit.,* p. 154.
7. G. Wolstenholme and M. O'Connor, eds., *Man in Africa,* Ciba Foundation Symposium (Boston: Little, Brown, 1965).
8. *Somalia: Survey of Technical Education,* UNESCO serial No. 1254 (New York: UNESCO, 1969).
9. K. Cahill, *Health on the Horn of Africa* (London: Spottiswoode, 1969).
10. R. F. Burton, *First Footsteps in East Africa,* 1856.

Health and
Economic Development

Mark Perlman

As I survey the development of economic thinking since the end of World War II, I am impressed by the point that the concept of the interdependency of nations is a logical extension of the development over the past 300 years of both our Western political culture and our experience of economic growth. Yet we seem to be finding, to our amazement, that the logic of both our culture and our experience is far less evident to people living in feudal political societies and *latifundia*-level economies than it is to us. Indeed, one of our major attempts since 1945 has been to find a value *numeraire* which provides a common denominator understandable both to "us," the richer industrialized nations, and to "them," the poorer, less economically developed nations. For want of a better tool we have tried (not always successfully) to use measurements of per capita economic well-being as that common denominator. As we have come to recognize the limitations of this simple economic index, we have also tried to give per capita economic well-being a health dimension, for good health

45

seems to us to be a *desideratum,* evident to everyone, irrespective of his culture or level of economic development. Consequently, international health programs have been repeatedly, but not with complete effectiveness, incorporated into considerations of the international *numeraire* which rich nations and poor nations have thought to use in their dialogues.

Regardless of the resolution of the technicalities involved,[1] the per capita "index" of economic well-being is a ratio between what is generally available for domestic consumption (goods and services for any purpose *including better individual health*) within a country (gross domestic product or GDP) and the population of that country (P), who exercise a greater or a smaller claim to participate in the consumption of the aforementioned product. This seemingly simple ratio GDP/P is not a comparison of two static numbers (i.e., GDP and P), rather it is a comparison of a growing numerator (GDP)[2] and a growing denominator (P),[3] and is far more complex than it seems at first glance. Generally the numerator and denominator do not grow at the same rates; if the former grows faster, life is generally easier (particularly if the benefits of the growth are distributed throughout the country's population).

Analyzing Economic Growth: Changes in the Numerator

Economic development is usually said to occur when there is any increase in production of goods or services. Normally such production, when undertaken by the private sector, is brought about by a difference in the price which consumers are willing to pay for it and its cost of production. Because there is often doubt about the eventual costs of production and the strength of demand, persons charged with planning economic development generally prefer to concentrate on goods or services that are characterized by a hardy demand, both for the present and the foreseeable future.

Costs are the result of the interaction of the following seven agents of production.[4]

1. Availability of raw natural resources, such as wood, ore, fertile soil, etc.
2. Accessibility of these resources—the degree of inexpensive transportation.
3. Availability of adequate technology—processes which make possible comparatively low costs of manufacture.
4. Availability of a population willing and able to provide the necessary degree of skilled labor.
5. Availability of power and water for industrial purposes.
6. Availability of capital at sufficiently low real interest rates to make investment an actuality.
7. Presence of managerial skill.

One may start by observing that under specific sets of conditions public health programs can play particularly critical roles in regard to the supply of several of these agents of production.

To illustrate, let us consider the economic development of several Brazilian communities.

The Amazon Experience. The history of rubber production in the Amazon Basin is well known. This area, originally the home of wild rubber, prospered during the latter decades of the nineteenth century as the world's demand for rubber grew. So great was the demand that vast sums of money were used to tempt impoverished persons to enter the jungle and expose themselves to diseases, particularly yellow fever and malaria, in order to market the crop. On a wall of the Manaus Opera House, itself a monument to the rubber boom, there is a plaque noting that in 1911 an Italian opera company lost all of its thirty members to yellow fever. But a world market price in excess of two dollars a pound (in 1907 it was $2.07) was sufficient to induce workers to enter the area. The bubble of prosperity broke around 1913 when Malayan plantation rubber began to be marketed in quantity. The Amazon Valley was quickly replaced as a source. Not only was it an unhealthy place for humans to live and work, but rubber trees (native to the Amazon) actually grew better in Malaya, where the rainfall pattern was more agreeable and where there were fewer leaf diseases.

In 1927 the Ford Motor Company attempted to reestablish the Amazon as a major source of supply. Its motivations for making the attempt were partly economic—they believed that they could produce it below market cost—and partly altruistic—they sought to bring an industry to an economically stagnant area. From the first, the Ford Motor Company met with difficulties. The soil was infertile and trees suffered from blight; the extraordinarily difficult living conditions raised the cost of hiring supervisory personnel; the labor force was ill-prepared for the kind of work needed; there was no natural factor (i.e., labor) market; and a wholly new technology had to be devised. Nonetheless by the beginning of World War II, the Ford Motor Company had planted 12,000 of the somewhat less than two million acres it held. The outbreak of hostilities in the Far East made the United States and its allies completely dependent once again upon the Amazon Basin for rubber. The Ford plantations at Belterra and Fordlandia could not begin to fill the need.

The United States Government then proposed to return to the method of supply used prior to the opening of the Malayan plantations, that is, to the gathering of wild rubber in the Amazon area. Medical knowledge had, of course, advanced considerably since 1910 and the United States Government was prepared to appropriate large sums to improve living conditions in the area as part of its policy to expand production. In full cooperation with the Brazilian government, it financed major campaigns to eradicate yellow fever and malaria, to purify the water supply, and to provide hospital service where formerly even the most basic medical services were unknown. Massive programs for these purposes were developed. Thus, a public health program came to the Amazon Basin.

At the same time the United States Government, faced with a

tremendous need for rubber, financed considerable research to develop a synthetic product. These efforts were successful; moreover, the early end of the war in the Pacific presaged the reentry of the Malayan rubber crop into the market, and thus the attempt to restore the Amazon to its earlier preeminence as a supplier was abandoned. Technological developments in the field of synthetic rubber further reduced the market price, spelling the doom of the Brazilian industry. Even though considerable progress had been made in improving public health conditions, expenditure on further development of the Brazilian rubber industry was uneconomic. The Ford Motor Company virtually gave away its $15,000,000 holdings for an insignificant portion of their worth, $250,000.

However, expenditures on malaria eradication, hospital services, and improved environmental sanitation in the Amazon Basin bore some positive economic results. In a few isolated areas, significant economic development occurred. Malaria eradication, for instance, on the island of Marajo opened that area to labor. At least two new types of economic activity developed. Cattle raising became a significant activity, resulting in the establishment of leather and fresh-meat markets in an area where no market had previously existed. Even more interesting than the new cattle industry, was the growth of a sawmill industry in the town of Breves. As far as we can tell, sawmill activity had previously been impossible because of endemic malaria. Elimination of the pestilence, or at any rate dimunition of its severity, made economic progress possible.

One other public health program in the Amazon Basin deserves specific mention. In cooperation with the mayor, a hospital was built at Santarem, a river community located approximately halfway between Belem and Manaus. For the first time adequate medical service became available, making the area a better place to live for trained personnel who would otherwise have refused to bring their families. Jute and hemp industries have subsequently been developed there. That similar developments have not occurred elsewhere in the Amazon Basin suggests that hospital service may be an essential prerequisite for industrial growth to begin; otherwise the technicians and managers necessary for this activity simply will not stay.

However, the most spectacular developments in the Amazon Basin in recent years did not depend in any great degree upon government public health programs. These developments were the peppercorn colony in Tome Açu and the ICOMI manganese mining operation in Amapa. They illustrate, moreover, both the importance of public health work in economic development and the possibilities of private financing of public health facilities. These developments were successful because of the general skill of their entrepreneurs in organizing the appropriate economic activity, including the establishment of privately financed public health programs.

The former was established by a Japanese group in 1928 when a land grant was obtained from the Para State government. About 270 families were sent out from Japan; within the next seven years all but 30 were either wiped out or driven away by malaria. The 30 families that remained managed to clear an area in the jungle, plant vines, and develop a technology adequate for the colony to prosper, but success did not come until after World War II.

Drawing upon the technical knowledge gained by the Brazilians and Americans from their wartime DDT program, the Japanese financed and developed their own public health scheme. By 1959 the colony was producing approximately 4,000 tons or about 10 per cent of the world market. It should be noted that although malaria was a serious problem, one which all but crushed the development, elimination of the disease was only a necessary, not a sufficient, condition for economic growth. Also needed were (1) entrepreneurs; (2) a labor force willing and able to work intelligently in the jungle environment; (3) sufficient capital to see the colony through its first twenty years until it reached sufficient size to realize some of the economies of scale; (4) the development of an appropriate technology to permit it to produce at low enough unit cost to compete in the market; and (5) an effective market demand.

In the Territory of Amapa within the past fifteen years, the world's most efficient manganese mining operation has been developed. The mine itself is located at Serra de Navio, from whence the ore is taken on seagoing carriers. ICOMI, the mining company, operates three communities, one at the mine, one midway between the mine and the port, and one at the port. The whole organization is on a vast scale and embodies the most modern technological adaptations. The effort was largely financed by a loan from the American Export-Import Bank.

The medical and public health programs, sponsored not by the government, but privately by ICOMI, are unquestionably the most advanced in the area. Yet the very success of this public health enterprise has, surprisingly enough, created problems hitherto unknown in the area. The drastic curtailment of infant mortality, without a program to keep the birth rate down, has led to serious overcrowding of homes and to the emotional exhaustion of mothers. Mental health has thus become a problem as prosperity has increased.

There are two points here. First, the economic success of the ICOMI in Amapa would have been hindered by an inadequate public health program. Second, solution of the traditional public health problems reveals an entirely new area for public health concern. The ICOMI-sponsored public health program, having solved the problems of environmental sanitation, the principal contagious diseases, and infant mortality, will have to be reconstituted to concentrate on family planning and mental hygiene.

Despite the economic development fostered by the publicly and privately financed public health programs in the Amazon Basin, investigations as well as discussions with Brazilian economists and engineers lead to the conclusion that there are great impediments to more rapid economic development in the area. These include a shortage of power, a deficiency of adequate entrepre-

neurial talent, absence of an agricultural technology adapted to
the rain-leached jungle soil, and a lack of transportation facilities
beyond the river banks. Thus, while the extension of malaria control might foster some additional economic developments, it
would seem to be economically wiser for the present to allocate
most of the scarce health resources to areas with a greater number
of the factors presently necessary for economic growth.

One can cite other examples of the ways that public health investment have aided *the numerator,*[5] but brevity requires moving
on to discussion of *the denominator*. Before doing so there is one
caveat about the numerator which must be identified. The implicit
premise here is that public health programs will be organized to
aid primarily the economically active segments of the population.
Because many public health planners refused to focus their efforts
on the economically productive, their programs seemed to Congress to be self-defeating insofar as they prevented people dying
from one kind of disease only to die from malnutrition. Congress
and the Administration then moved to cut off public health AID
programs. The discovery of new means of fertility control plus
wiser public health planning has led, fortunately, to the resump-
tion of public health international assistance. Policies coming
from this "second thought" require a capacity for decision-taking
and -holding. Otherwise these same health measures *may still* (I
shall argue below that they also *may not*) have the impact of increasing the denominator (i.e., the population) faster than they increase the numerator (i.e., the annual flow of goods and services).
This point is so critical that it is worth repetition:

Unless a public health program is carefully designed to help
those whose activities are in highest demand, the effect of curing
the ill may merely increase the size of the dependent population
and thus reduce the per capita level of national or regional product. In the recent past, indiscriminate provision of public health
aid has caused some Washington foreign assistance administrators
to look with disfavor, if not with horror, on international public
health programs.

To this, the first answer is simply to note that public health programs can be designed to aid one segment rather than the total population. If such be the desire, then a useful set of criteria should be developed to aid in the process. In "spotting shots" there is virtue in concentrating first on teen-agers (particularly those who have some education) and economically active adults. The result will be greater production—a part of which can then be used on further broadening health service coverage.

Analyzing Population Growth: Changes in the Denominator

The denominator of our changing comparison is the initial size and rate of growth of the population. Populations, quite obviously, grow because rates of in-migration and birth collectively exceed the combined effects of the rates of out-migration and death. Migration, both in and out of nations, is to some extent subject to social control. Births and deaths have been considerably less subject to social control if at all. Recent medical advances, contrary to earlier hopes, have not made social reduction of birth rates universally more effective, even though the rapid spread of medical techniques has had a remarkably noticeable impact on lowering age-specific death ratios in the younger (0 to 45) age groups.

Let us discuss changes in death rates first because the topic is the easier to handle. Modern antibiotic- and electrolytic balance-medicine has assured longevity to millions who only a decade or two ago would almost surely have been "scheduled" for death in childhood, adolescence, or young adulthood. More recent discoveries increasing acreage production of cereals (rice and wheat) have done much to assure that those who have been saved from death-by-disease will have enough (or almost enough) to eat. Thus, death is no longer the "guarantor" of the small denominator it once was.

The other way to decrease the denominator is to encourage restriction of live births. Such a policy can be accomplished by using a spectrum of means—ranging from easy abortion and encouragement of the use of contraceptives to providing young girls with job alternatives to early marriage. Listing these means has not been the problem; in many centuries and in many cultures those who wanted to restrict rates of population growth (P) have, it is historically apparent, managed to accomplish their objective without the "pill" or the I.U.D. What we seem unable to understand is the incentive system, both direct and indirect, to lead impoverished populations to assign fertility control a high priority. Instead, we have largely concentrated on helping those who are already convinced.

In another essay[6] I argue that a historical condition for the transition from high to low fertility rates may well have been misidentified. The usual theory says that a fall in the 0 to 20-year-old age-specific death rates will automatically lead to a fall in fertility rates. This theory suggests that increased rates of child survival brings about less "need" for child creation. I conclude, instead, that it is not reduction in mortality—but rather reduction in morbidity-rates among adults (numbers able to work regularly) that may be the critical factor; not, as is so widely believed, reduction in morbidity rates among the young. Reduction in morbidity rates means more regular employment and greater production. Suffice it here to refer to my conclusion; considerations of space in this essay preclude spelling out the argument. The inference of the conclusion is, however, critical. *Public health programs which serve to increase productive economic capacity (particularly when combined with educational programs aimed at the same objective) may lead to dimunition of the desire to reproduce at the accustomed historically high fertility rates.* This thesis is not yet empirically confirmed; we lack the necessary data. But it has an attractiveness inherent in the way I read the history of countries and economies where demographic transition has occurred.

An Additional Consideration

Aside from economic development, international medical aid programs have another rationale. Epidemic disease does not respect national boundaries; moreover, increased speed of travel (e.g., jet planes) makes disease conditions in East Pakistan an obvious threat not only to India, but also to Western Europe and North America. Thus, international medical aid programs become a form of first-line (nonderivative, as above) national policies. The economics of this kind of situation is, as I have noted above, simply individual and then "parent" country self-interest; it is cheaper to prevent epidemics abroad than it is to prevent them (and certainly to cure them) at home.

There is another rationale for the development of medical aid programs which has made them popular with many host countries. It is the historical experience that public health programs lead to the centralization of social organization.[7] This is no small point. Both historically and at the present time there are few activities which so clearly tie people to central governments as do centrally administered health programs both on the clinical and on the preventive medical sides. I refer to this aspect as the patently "political approach" to national health programs. The term *political* may be a misnomer, but it is one which serves my purpose as well as any other phrase.

Seventeenth-century political thought in England and Scotland was dominated by John Hobbes' assertion that society was organized to prevent one brutish man (invariably a knave) from hitting each and every other man (also brutish and a knave) from behind. Thus, to prevent the law of the jungle (in reality the absence of any kind of law except brutal opportunism) from prevailing, societies were formed (individuals agreed on social contract) and governments were formed (government contract). Hobbes' estimate of the inelegant nature of our species did not set well with the moralists of the era, but they were not, I fear, really able to offer any other rational argument for social development unless it was God's will (and most of them defined God's will as superrational and certainly not something which could regularly be depended upon).

It was Adam Smith, whom my philosopher friends assure me

was a "nonpersuasive" (meaning second-rate) moralist, who suggested a supplementary reason for men's cooperation. Smith did not know whether men were really as brutish as Hobbes said they were, but he did argue that the existence of large groups permitted specialization of function and that such specialization vastly increased per individual output (productivity).

By the nineteenth century, problems of public administration were no longer left to the not very active consciences of the hereditary princes, nor were they being solved very satisfactorily by being ignored. Instead, a new mentality seemed to be developing, a mentality which believed with Socrates that if you want your shoes to be mended, go to a cobbler; and, if you want your government run, go to skilled civil servants.

The difficulty, however, was that there were all too few civil servants of merit and all too frequent jealousies of their assertion of power. Thus the problem of social organization came down to convincing the rank and file that they had to give real power to civil servant specialists in order to protect each individual's most basic rights. These basic rights, I hasten to add, were said to be life, liberty, and property, but of these life was the key one. With life one could claim the other two; without life, the other two seemed to be abstractions.

It is my thesis here that those most interested in sociopolitical reform in the nineteenth century discovered that if their demand for change was tied to the need to protect life, then their case was all but won. Sir Edwin Chadwick[8] understood this truth quite early and his reliance upon the 1842 *Sanitary Report*[9] was simply a manifestation of this realization. But it was not the evil of squalor and disease that Chadwick portrayed, nor was it the threat to those with wealth from the poor and sick (Chadwick did not believe in the germ or bacteriological theory of disease). Rather, it was the specific fear of cholera that he used to give edge to his argument.

Cholera, as we know the disease now, need not be a mysterious killer able to strike the healthy dead in a very few hours. Now we realize how it is transmitted and we appreciate the way its dehydrating effects kill. In Chadwick's day, Snow's important discovery of how it spreads was unknown; in fact, von Pettenkoffen, the great Munich scientist, never did accept Snow's explanation. And the principles of dehydration, so critical to the prevention of cholera mortality, have been generally available for typical use for less than two decades.

A century ago cholera was so dramatic a threat to life that wise political administrators used it for their own purposes. In other words, disease and the desire for health became the vehicles which political reformers used to accomplish their preferred objectives.

In our own era, even though the hysteria about disease seems less, the same mechanism is still employed. I cite two quite separate instances of its use.

In Cuba after the fall of the Batista regime, the Castro government, evidently seeking a quick impact program, increased the spending on public health to the point where each month it spent a multiple of what the previous regime had spent in decades. Who could say that the Castroites were indifferent to life, when they gave such a great priority to preservation of life? And if life was purchased at some expense to property or liberty—what matter? Life is basic, and as such it seems to be the political rule of thumb used by most men. I am told, but have no way of checking, that what is true in Cuba is no less true in Red China. If so, the aforementioned rule of thumb may even be a political principle.

The second case is closer to home. Since about 1950 the United States Supreme Court has been more dedicated to the principle of individual liberty than the Court seems ever to have been in its long past. Nonetheless, there has been one single exception to this dedication which is part of the record.

Shortly after World War II an employee of the City of Baltimore conceived a program to arrest decay of property values. He suggested simply that Baltimore enforce its many building codes. To accomplish this, several building inspectors were assigned to one particular area. In the course of one such inspector's duties he saw a rat disappear into a building on a piece of private property. He pursued the rodent. As he had no judicial warrant to enter the property, the property owner not only refused to honor the directive that the inspector issued, but denied the propriety of any inspector's entering private premises without either the owner's permission or judicial warrant.

Ultimately the Supreme Court heard the case and ruled at that time to accept the doctrine that whereas the police may not come and go as their professional instinct leads them, health inspectors may do so. The Court has since backed away from this ruling, but I think the point is still largely valid; in other words, a rodent or the suspicion of a health hazard (and the one I suggest has not been proven to be the same as the other) can be used to augment administrative powers in a way which much stronger allegations of the antisocial characteristics of organized crime and even the intelligence apparatus of generally hostile powers cannot be used. Such is the mystique of health and how it has and can be used by those interested in centralizing or making more efficient public administration.

The thrust of this essay is the argument that health measures, national or international in origin, affect economic well-being in several different (and certainly noncompeting ways). They can serve to increase output as well as to diminish the rate of population growth. They can serve to prevent epidemic disease crossing borders. And, finally, they can tie populations to national government.

Notes

1. There are many anomolies in national income measurement; e.g., when a man marries his housekeeper (and ceases to pay her wages), national income falls, while presumably the production of goods and services is, if anything, increased. This anomaly (along with many others) is known to economists; this in-

formation should come as no surprise to noneconomists—it is an indication of economists' awareness
　of the chinks in their disciplinary fortress.
2. G$\overset{\bullet}{\text{D}}$P is the relative ratio of growth of GDP: where G$\overset{\bullet}{\text{D}}$P
　　= d (GĠP/dt x 1/GDP.
3. Similar to 2. above: where $\overset{\bullet}{\text{P}}$ = d$\overset{\bullet}{\text{P}}$/dt . 1/P.
4. Parts of this section are taken from my essay, "Some
　　Aspects of Public Health Programs in Underdeveloped Nations," in Bureau of Public Health Economics and Department of Economics (University
　　of Michigan), *The Economics of Health and Medical Care,* Proceedings of the Conference on the
　　Economics of Health and Medical Care, May 10-12
　　(Ann Arbor: University of Michigan Press, 1964),
　　pp. 286-305.
5. See explanation of the equation given above.
6. A *Festschrift* for Edgar M. Hoover to be published by
　　Gordon and Breach Science Publishers (New York
　　City).
7. The rationale of this argument is spelled out in an as yet
　　unpublished essay, "The Methodology of Public
　　Health Investment."
8. *Ibid.*
9. Edwin Chadwick, *Report on the Sanitary Condition of
　　the Labouring Population of Great Britain* [1842],
　　edited by M. W. Flinn (Edinburgh: Edinburgh University Press).

Educative and Preventive
Medical Programs

Edward E. Swanstrom

I CONFESS TO AN understandable diffidence—even reluctance—
in joining medical experts and diplomats dealing with medicine
and diplomacy. The editor of this book deliberately included a
person who is alert to the multiple problems of the developing
world but is not a medical professional. As the executive director
of a large American voluntary agency, and as one member of a
council of 24 voluntary agencies, I decided to offer what I might
call "Notes from the Medical Underground."

My vantage point of observation is the dark underside of life—
the isolated rural areas, urban centers newly swollen with rural
migrants, and refugee communities located in 30 countries between the tropics of Cancer and Capricorn. Because of the absolute urgency of scientific direction, our agency has added medical personnel to our staff in Africa and Central America; I shall
draw on their reports and on the reports and critiques of field
personnel in what I say.

In the past quarter of a century, since I first began visiting our projects in India, the Philippines, Africa, and Latin America, there has been a tremendous surge in medical aid from private, governmental, and intergovernmental sources. In the days after World War II, the health centers we visited were mostly scattered and heroic outposts conducted by various religious groups.

I gratefully note recent signs of interdenominational cooperation and planning. Much more is needed.

Many of the missionary medical centers dealt with the old scourges that had afflicted these areas from time immemorial. Leprosy is a prime example. Denominational bodies have been dunned for generations for the support of hospitals for the segregation and care of lepers. Perhaps because leprosy is a biblical disease it has elevated the international Christian community to a worldwide preeminence in the care of a disorder that made outcasts of those afflicted with it.

Progress in this one field has been dramatic. Instead of collecting the enormous funds necessary for the construction of a leprosarium and the administrative planning necessitated by a staff of lay or religious missionaries, the approach today is simpler and, I feel, more effective. Take the well-known case of Calcutta, where all the health problems of Asia meet in one choking and glutted city. Little nests of lepers cluster with their families in many of the *bustees* or slum sections. The lepers sally out to beg at certain times and in certain areas, outside churches, temples, and mosques. The well members of the family often hold jobs as food-handlers and servants, so that leprosy has appeared in some of the wealthiest families of the city.

A new group, headed by Mother Teresa, a woman of Albanian origin, asked for a mobile clinic so that she could visit the groups of leprosy patients she had met in her *bustee* schools and training centers. Rather than expect the afflicted people to come to a center, the clinic went to them. The Institute for Tropical Diseases of Calcutta supplied doctors, and American sources supplied a key factor: food. When a significant amount of food was given to each patient and his family, the number of patients increased enormously. Oxford Famine Relief joined the project to supply the latest antileprosy medicaments in quantity.

Will this development resolve the leprosy problem of this refugee-swollen city? Of course not, but the improved nutrition and regular treatment will accomplish two very desirable goals: a certain number of leprosy patients will be rendered noninfectious, and a large number of what are referred to as "untainted children" will be saved from the affliction through the educational adjuncts of the program. After a few years of cooperation between Mother Teresa, the Institute of Tropical Medicine, and two voluntary agencies, the Calcutta community became interested and is now concerned with housing and work for the hitherto invisible lepers.

In Korea, the rate of leprosy is very high. Persons do not come forward for treatment because they fear being branded for the rest of their lives. A counterpart voluntary group with the aid of the American Catholic Medical Mission Board operates five mobile clinics, called by their clients "skin clinics." Through this service skin diseases are cared for and the first signs of leprosy are detected. The developments cited indicate not only the evolution of medical programs but the delivery of medical care to those who would not otherwise receive it and who would almost inevitably infect family and community. They are also evidence of a particular service of the voluntary agency: namely, the "finger-pointing exercise."

Although it lacks larger resources available to governments and intergovernmental organizations, the voluntary agency is often strong on personnel who are close to the realities of a given area. Such personnel, sometimes a sister-doctor, a few trained nurses, or a midwife, will often dare to start a pilot project that is no more than a finger pointing at a huge unmet need. The incessant finger-pointing inherent in a manifestly inadequate but zealous health unit often stimulates communities and official organizations into taking more adequate action.

Certainly the new mobility of peoples, often forced, as in massive exiles and expulsions, often voluntary, as in the movement of families and parts of families to the cities of Latin America, Africa, and Asia has demanded a mobility in medical programs. A vastly increased mobility is needed. How else can even emergency medical care be brought to the poor who inhabit new agglomerations of shanties and huts around such Latin American cities as Buenos Aires, Bogotá, and Caracas? Increased mobility will enable international voluntary agencies to serve better the more than 17,000,000 refugees who straddle the world as a virtual "refugee nation"; this may help develop a new "medicine for the poor."

The middle-class doctor who waits passively for his adequately housed middle-class patients to come to his consultation room has little or no relevance for the developing world. And yet the doctor who is trained in the United States all too often goes back to the main metropolitan areas of his own country and attempts to develop this type of lucrative and tragically selective medical practice. Such incidents put in doubt the transferability of medical training from developed to lesser developed areas, not only in the case of doctors but of nursing and administrative personnel.

Thus far I have been referring to the curative aspect of medicine, and this, of course, is where medicine began. In the developing world, unless medicine can move dramatically from its heavy emphasis on the simply curative, it will isolate itself from the realities of living. Even the witch doctor stresses preventive medicine in his propitiatory rites to the spirits.

Let me attempt to clarify what I mean. Our field staff has stressed to me that the medical profession must think, in the developing world, in terms of educative and preventive programs over and above the practice of cure. Further, much of this education must be in the fields of nutrition and public health. Dr. René Dubos has expressed "a deeply felt conviction that the extent of health improvement that ensues from building ultramodern hospitals with up-to-date equipment is probably trivial in comparison with the results that can be achieved at much lower cost by providing all infants and children with well-balanced food, sanitary conditions, and a stimulating environment."[1] We add to this the need for educative medicine.

Our medical advisor in Africa, Dr. Carlo Capone, has written a monograph entitled *Child Health and Food Aid in Developing Countries* in which he gives evidence that the child under five bears the chief brunt of the social, economic, and nutritional problems of deficit areas. On the other hand, the child of this age lags far behind in benefits accruing from the economic development of a country. The only chance he has of receiving benefits is for the country to plan a *direct* and *specific* program on his behalf. Current programs demonstrate that national health care is first focused on the productive segment of the population. Stacy May says, "Tropical medicine is the 'midwife of economic progress' in the underdeveloped areas of the world. Where mass diseases are brought under control, productivity tends to increase . . . through augmenting strength and ambition to work. . . ."[2]

Senegal, whose national budget can afford no more than 30 cents per inhabitant per year for medical aid and vaccines, cannot afford a health project designed specifically for the "under fives" in the population. Fortunately, governments such as our own are recognizing malnutrition for what it really is: the cause not only of a large percentage of disease problems but also of irreversible damage to physical and even mental development. The onslaught on hunger and malnutrition both here and abroad is a most important step in preventive medicine.

Our own agency under the leadership of Dr. Carlo Capone has created a Child Health Scheme for children under five in Senegal and in almost all the countries of sub-Saharan Africa. At least 600 clinics are presently engaged in providing extra nutrition to mothers of preschool children. The foods come from the stocks of the U.S. Food for Peace. The contact with the mothers in their fertility period offers an unexampled opportunity for training in child and family nutrition. In addition to its supply of high-protein foods each clinic or health center uses scales and charts (known as

Health Indicators) to plot the weight changes of the child in such a way that even an illiterate mother can see graphic indications of her child's health.

To women of child-bearing age the opportunity is given to learn basic hygiene as well as the prerequisites to having and rearing a healthy child. Dr. Capone, who points out that the child is the chief victim of underdevelopment, maintains that unless practical steps are taken for infants and children here and now *it is the child who will defeat all other development programs.* This is a sobering thought as we enter the second development decade of the United Nations in 1970.

It may be helpful to consider the implications of this warning and to take action. First, the prime need of developing countries is for supplemental supplies from outside them. These countries cannot provide the extra foods needed to combat the vast malnutrition. The extra foods exist in such rich and developed nations as Canada, the United States, and parts of Europe and Australia. If there is a focus on the needs of the children under five, plans can be made for the transfer of the needed and available foods, including powdered milk and high-protein cereals, from the rich countries to the poor. Health Indicators are already being printed for nations in Asia as well as Africa.

The latest extension of this type of program in nutritional education is being prepared for six Central American countries with the cooperation of the U.S. Agency for International Development. The general supervision is in the hands of Dr. Frances Rothert, our medical and public health advisor for Central America. Food will again be the real "hinge" of the program.

The availability of food ensures the presence of mothers with children under five. We cannot expect illiterate mothers to come to the village school or church hall for a lecture. The food is also a spur to community leaders; it can thus spark a many-pronged effort not only for nutritional improvement but for community action in general.

The educational program will eventually reach tens of thousands of the most deprived families. These are the families whose access to curative medicine is minimal. For them the preventive aspect of the nutritional education program is crucial. What is especially significant about the organization of the growing network of under-five health schemes is that a single doctor can put it in motion. That same doctor, tied to a stationary clinic and a line of patients, would play a far less valuable role in promoting health in any tropical country.

Another medical channel in the developing world is the radio. The omnipresence of the transistor radio has been put to marvelous use. Village mothers in the most remote sections of Colombia, for instance, have learned child care and elementary sanitation in lectures transmitted through the transistor. Arrangements were made for village women to listen in groups and to take a test at the end of a given course. When clothing was offered as prizes, thousands more participated.

Dr. Capone is not alone in pointing out that "Foods are the principal item the developing nations are short of and will be short of for many years to come. . . . It is also the commodity that the developed world can produce, and must produce, above commercial requirements."

Those of us who see our United States overseas aid budget shrink each year (while our arms budget has grown until it swallows well over half of our federal budget) will become more and more vocal about the need for a radical change in priorities. Maximum utilization of the food resources of developed countries calls for larger foreign-aid outlays from the United States as well as the provision of skilled personnel who will be available to places such as Latin America, Africa, and Asia and to their public-health officials.

In this connection I must also mention another facet of the utilization of foods from developed lands. There is need to prepare the foods in such a way that they may be immediately usable by the recipient. When, in the late 1940's and early 1950's, the United States had enormous surpluses of wheat, the voluntary agencies could obtain large supplies of flour for their aid programs in the hungry areas of the world. But flour presumes baking, and millions of the poorest people—Asians, for example—had nothing resembling an oven. Voluntary agency leaders, from their close acquaintance with the living habits of the needy, explained that wheat would have to be supplied in a form that could be cooked by boiling. It was suggested that the wheat be supplied in the form of bulgur wheat, a cracked wheat used in tropical areas since biblical times. Bulgur wheat has become the basis for many development programs in India and elsewhere in the past decade and a half.

Many new forms of food, especially such high-protein concentrates as CSM (Corn-Soya-Milk), and various fish flours are among the contributions that science has made to nutrition. Science has shown that in many deficient areas of the earth local resources that were never believed to have nutritional value can be processed for human consumption. These untapped sources can be tapped only through committed research.

Even more fruitful results can be achieved in the future if funds are channeled more liberally into research for projects of human welfare and nutrition. Here is where the medical men today must raise their voices if we are to have a better tomorrow, or even any tomorrow. Who can estimate the billions of dollars that went into research to produce hydrogen bombs that can cremate alive the populations of the world's greatest cities? The inhabitants of the developing world are very sure that such weapons can be delivered. They have every reason to doubt that in the next development decade there will be much improvement in the delivery of even the most basic of health services.

Lest I sound apocalyptic, let me sound a note of hope. At the Child Welfare Conference held in Stockholm this year, the only essentially cheerful note concerned progress in the health field in developing countries. Mortality rates and infant mortality specifically have decreased in the last several decades. The decrease is attributable to the fight against endemo-epidemic and infectious diseases, and the efforts made in the field of environmental sanitation, health, and *nutritional education.*

The medical profession must, then, be constantly looking toward the future, using every available means to prod society away from its ignorant, lazy, and even lethal tendencies and toward those aspects of knowledge and practice that strengthen and conserve life. This is not easy. It would be much easier for a medical man to cure one by one the cases of worms that debilitate his patients than to mount a tiring and difficult *campaign* against intestinal worms in a province of India or in the rural part of Taiwan. Vigorous campaigns are needed to promote the medicine of the poor and the medicine of the illiterate.

Someone commenting on an East African scene described a condition which kills 14 per cent of all babies before the tenth day of life, namely, tetanus of the umbilical cord. Curative medicine using all forms of modern treatment *might* save four out of ten cases, whereas antitetanus injections will immunize the fortunate mothers. This is preventive medicine. Teaching natives not to use dirty bamboo knives in severing umbilical cords could save thousands of mothers and infants. This is educative medicine.

Every doctor in a developing area must be in great measure a public and environmental expert if he is to avoid the stigma of being a sort of commercial agent who sells his medical product to the highest bidders. As a man with scientific credentials he should play the role of a guru for society in all health matters: in the necessity for latrines, for example. No aspect of the environment should be beyond his ken—and he must become a multidisciplinary man if he is to talk to the community as a guru.

Thus far I have been discussing preventive medicine as it relates to education in such basic matters as nutrition. I should like to stress a necessity of life as basic as food. Dr. Dubos tells us, "There are indications that general dietary improvement, better practices of infant feeding and handling, and *simply an abundant supply of water,* would be a far more effective and less costly approach to the control of intestinal disorders, than are prophylaxis and treatment with drugs and vaccines."[3]

The phrase "an abundant supply of water" is hardly more than a dream in the *favelas, barriadas,* or *callampas* that have mushroomed around Latin America's cities where the poorest of the poor often have to buy their drinking water from vendors. Abundant water is hardly more than a dream in great parts of India where, according to a recent conference at Wardha, only 120,000 of India's 570,000 villages have a good and adequate supply of drinking water. Of the remaining 450,000 villages, it is estimated that one third have inadequate sources of drinking water and another third have unhygienic sources. The last third have no sources at all, meaning that the villagers have to fetch all water from a distance of a mile or more.

A doctor serving in such an area might well make himself an expert on wells and water levels. Our director for India worked with Indian officials and representatives of other voluntary agencies and decided on a health project to mark the Gandhi centennial year of 1969. Again, food became the "hinge" on which the whole program turned. The wells were to be dug in such parched areas as Bihar by voluntary effort, but the workers needed supplementary food. Here again, Food for Peace mobilized people to participate. Squads of workers recruited by Indian voluntary agencies in the Gandhian tradition constructed 2,000 wells in Bihar alone. Close to 4,000 wells have been constructed in other areas of India. Of course a cash outlay was necessary to purchase the cement and other supplies needed to complete the wells. Here is a challenge to a medical team: to motivate and stimulate support for construction of wells for the villages of India without wells and for those villages whose water supply is unhygienic. What a massive work of preventive medicine that represents.

But that leads us to the question of motivation, and that is where all such schemes for the betterment of man either flounder or sail into port. Motivation comes out of our commitment, out of the deepest recesses of our consciences. I hope that many more professional medical people will be motivated to join people-to-people programs of the long-standing service groups that have a mission to raise people by their educative and preventive medical programs around the world, and that they will offer aid through a permanent corps of medical professionals to assure constant attention to the medical problems of the developing world. I make this point to emphasize the need for *longer terms* of volunteer or semivolunteer services so that the personnel can absorb the language or the special mores of an area. Our young people now are motivated by a desire for service rather than profit; they desire peace rather than conflict. Even the medical profession should open its doors for young people to serve the needs of the poorer nations in paramedical assistance as a form of field work. I also hope there will be a unification of the efforts of all religious groups in the planning and execution of their medical programs so that they can present a united appeal to governments, foundations, and specialized agencies of the United Nations.

Nikolai A. Berdyaev, the Russian philosopher, has said that the question of bread for one's neighbor is not a material question but a spiritual one. I accept that in its widest application, for I believe that the question of healing our neighbor in this global village is a spiritual matter. The spiritual eye must see the whole human family as actually one; it must pierce us with pain at another's suffering. Otherwise how can we be moved to the healing acts that our sick society and our sick world so tragically need?

Notes

1. R. Dubos, *Man and His Environment,* Scientific Publication No. 131 (Washington: Pan American Health Organization, 1966), pp. 7-8.
2. S. May, *Concepts* (Cologne, Germany: Medicus Mundi).
3. Dubos, *op. cit.,* pp. 9-10.

America's International Medical Programs

The Ideal and the Real

George I. Lythcott

T HE subject of American programs of medical assistance for developing countries is one of considerable importance and one in which I have a deep and abiding interest. In my view such programs can have, on the one hand, vast positive implications and rewards and can become a real source of pride for both donor and recipient; on the other hand, without thorough cognizance of the delicate nature of international affairs, without proper thought in its planning and attention to detail in its implementation, official American involvement in international medical programs can indeed become a fiasco.

My experience in the tropics extended over the seven-year period between June 1962 and June 1969; during that time I was stationed in Accra, Ghana, and later in Lagos, Nigeria. I still have continuing involvement in West Africa, which takes me back to the area from time to time, though on a different basis. My responsibilities involved all of West and Central Africa (except for

73

Portuguese Guinea) with limited experience in East and South-Central Africa as well. West and Central Africa is the vast territory bounded on the north by the Sahara Desert, on the west by the Atlantic Ocean, on the south by the Gulf of Guinea and the Bight of Benin, and on the east by the Congo River. This area is inhabited by an estimated 120 million people who speak more than 500 major tribal dialects; the official language of this area, however, is English, French, or Spanish. By 1962 all these countries except Equatorial Guinea had recently become independent of their colonial governments, although the influence of these governments was still manifest to a greater or lesser degree within most of them. By 1962, however, at least three of these newly independent nations had for all practical purposes repudiated the fundamental ideologies of France and Britain.

The ecology of this nineteen-country area varies from sandy desert land, with nomadic tribesmen roving willy-nilly across country borders in search of water or commerce, to tropical rainforest country, inundated with up to 400 inches of rain annually and inhabited by a virtually stationary population. Customs, culture, and the rhythm of day-to-day living are represented by patterns almost as numerous as the dialects. This cultural heritage, unchanged for centuries, is a source of great pride for each tribe and tribesman. There are several fairly large port and capital cities with quite a cosmopolitan air, and the language, customs, and culture of the ages have inevitably become so dissipated in these urban melting pots that a casual visitor to such an area could easily be completely unaware of the very different perspectives, values, and attitudes that make Africa the exciting continent that it is. Common to all these countries, however, are economic instability, poverty, and disease.

My experiences were based on two American international medical programs: the first, a research laboratory created through a bilateral agreement between an agency of the U.S. Public Health Service and one of the independent governments in West Africa; the second, a regional program for all nineteen West and Central

African countries, under the general auspices of the Agency for International Development but under the technical direction of a bureau of the United States Public Health Service.

The nineteen-country regional program for the eradication of smallpox has been eminently successful; it is reputed by some to be not only the best medical program mounted by the government of the United States in the developing countries, but also one of the most dramatic and successful American foreign-assistance programs ever—a testimony to the enthusiasm, dedication, knowledge, and meticulous attention to detail of those responsible for it. On November 30, 1969, in the little market village of Burbon, Niger, the 100 millionth vaccination was given, less than three years after the program had begun and more than one year ahead of the timetable the project had set for itself.

The research laboratory, by contrast, was considerably less successful for both the donor and the recipient, culminating for all practical purposes in a premature withdrawal of American personnel. This program, unfortunately, was doomed from its inception by an unusual set of circumstances that included some naïvete, ignorance, and questionable judgment on the parts of many, including myself. Further, the original agreement was drawn up and the American team recruited and dispatched at a time when diplomatic relations between the governments concerned were extremely tenuous. In addition, the scientist responsible for this program in the host country was himself a political refugee from his native country, and his political ideologies were completely antagonistic to those of the West—especially the United States. With more forethought and planning, and especially at a different time in political history, this could have been a most successful venture. Its dedicated senior scientists deserved a better fate.

Despite the second program's lack of success, however, *both* programs offer valuable experiences—some positive, some negative—for medical-assistance programs. Additional insights were provided during this period by my constant exposure to other official and private-sector medical programs in West Africa, including the Peace Corps and the whole spectrum of missionary effort. My observations, therefore, issue from all these experiences and reflect the pertinent practical issues that have crystallized during the last several years.

I use the terms "official American programs" or "official programs" in this discussion to refer to programs federally supported through active government agencies such as the Agency for International Development (AID), the Peace Corps, and the military—as distinct from medical programs sponsored by private groups, including missionary activity. Before approaching some of the practical aspects of the official American medical experience in emerging countries, I should like to examine the relation between this experience and the broad issues of politics and diplomacy. For these are the issues that significantly influence international medical programs, and discussion of them is essential in creating a frame of reference for my subsequent observations.

By technical definition, politics and diplomacy are not synonymous. "Politics" carries the unfavorable connotations of deviousness, of capriciousness, of expediency, and of partisan scheming. "Diplomacy," on the other hand, is reserved for the epitome of sophisticated social intercourse and it somehow seems very grand, even exemplary, and most palatable indeed. In practical parlance and in colloquial use, however, the onus of politics frequently attaches itself to diplomacy. It is important in this discussion, then, to recognize that to many people these terms are kissing cousins. This will help us appreciate the problems inherent in a discussion of medicine and diplomacy in the tropics. One could not hope to find two more incongruous bedfellows than medicine and politics—with medicine enunciating the brotherhood of man under the Hippocratic oath and politics enunciating its philosophies of expediency and factionalism. Yet in my experience I found them inseparable.

Dr. Kevin M. Cahill, in his Introduction to this book, stated, "Anyone visiting or working in a foreign country becomes involved—willingly or unwillingly, wittingly or unwittingly—in the political intercourse of his native and the host nation." A tourist, an itinerant working student, a sailor calling in port are all similarly affected. When that person visiting or working in a foreign country is an American, representing the richest and one of the most powerful nations in the world, it is difficult for him to escape the onus of being a political animal—no matter how apolitical he might be or may feel in this situation. Further, when an American is an official government representative visiting or working in an emerging country, the responsibility of coping with the politics of the United States and the host nation becomes impossible to escape. An official American in medicine overseas is no more and no less fortunate in this respect than his counterparts in agriculture, technology, education, or business enterprise. Medicine delivered in this context has no special license that would elevate it beyond this realm.

This posture—which sometimes attracts suspicion, sometimes antagonism—may on the other hand force the official American into the role of a savior, a harbinger of all solutions—and he may well fall heir to the ensuing disappointment when "all" things fail to materialize. The thrust of the American position on issues must never be underestimated, even when our judgment is being made solely in the context of American affairs and when no real attempt is being made to influence the position of other nations. The U.N. Food and Agriculture Organization, for example, has been deeply concerned by the reaction in many emerging countries to the American position on DDT. Because the United States decided to ban the use of DDT by 1971 for reasons we all know, the developing countries are suggesting that they must take the same position—thus discounting the necessity of DDT and dieldrin for their proved beneficial effects on health, agriculture, and economics in these countries.

Most physicians feel that medicine is a pure discipline which, ideally, should be extracted from the suspicion and vagaries that surround other forms of foreign assistance and that medical aid should be offered solely according to the needs of the recipient, rather than according to the political strategies of the donor nation. Moreover, we know well the great need for medical assistance to the emerging countries, and while one can hardly separate the priorities for assistance in health, education, technology, or agriculture, it is evident that health is the common denominator for the effective implementation of all these. We know that infectious diseases and malnutrition, singly and especially in combination, impose the greatest threat to life. Further, accumulating evidence indicates the direct relation between malnutrition and mental retardation—that malnutrition is capable of producing irreversible damage to the learning apparatus of children. Thus when we consider the ecology of human societies, physical well-being must be considered one of the most important limiting factors in this dynamic equilibrium.

We know that half the deaths in the developing countries occur among children under six years of age. In many African countries a mother must bear five children to assure that even one reaches the age of 15. We know that in Northeast Brazil, 48 percent do not survive the first year of life; by the age of four, 63 percent have succumbed. In parts of Southeast Asia 40 percent of the children die of disease in their first four years. This proportion of deaths is not reached in the United States until the age of 60.

Thus the potential for spectacular improvement in the health of the populations of emerging countries stems from two factors: (1) the health problems are so great to begin with, and (2) the present facilities and technology for dealing with them are generally so limited. Medical assistance, then, should be provided because the need is there—a lesson learned long ago by the missionary groups in their broad and redounding experience in the emerging countries. When the missionary groups first ventured into the underexplored areas of the world, medical personnel generally accompanied the missionaries abroad for the sheer survival of the clergy. Survival in those days was of paramount importance—in Accra, Ghana, there is a cemetery which was used only for the Europeans who arrived during the early nineteenth century. The gravestones are marked with the date of arrival in Accra and the date of death; all but three of some 250 persons succumbed during the first year in the tropics. Indeed, the coast of West Africa earned the name "The White Man's Grave."

As the years passed and medical knowledge increased, the physicians in the missionary groups, due to their growing familiarity with the communities they had come to love, began responding on an ad hoc basis to the desperate health needs of the indigenous population. More recently church boards have changed their emphasis from proselytizing, with medical assistance as a secondary goal, to providing medical assistance as a separate objective with no strings attached, in concert with the primary goal of proselytizing. This medical assistance now often includes preventive as well as curative medicine. That some identity has been lost in this change in focus has disturbed the international Christian community not at all.

Today's official agencies would do well to heed this imperative: to heal the sick *because they are sick*. It took the Peace Corps several years to embrace this point of view. Like the missionaries, the Peace Corps originally recruited physicians solely for the medical care of Peace Corps volunteers. The Peace Corps too has been through the intermediate ad hoc phase, but it now expects to mount structured medical programs in public health for its host communities, with the same sort of emphasis and care given to its successful projects in education, agriculture, and so on.

Nonetheless, even if government agencies do gradually respond directly to the pressing health needs of the host communities, medical-assistance programs delivered in this setting will still carry political overtones. If we are to operate official medical programs, we must be prepared to accept this political element as a fact of daily life; otherwise we must go outside the government enclave altogether and create new vehicles for the delivery of medical assistance. I realize that creating mechanisms outside the political environment by no means guarantees freedom from politics. It would, however, reduce the political onus to a level with which most people here and abroad could live.

The operation of medical-aid programs within the official government setting, however, seems to be the working reality for the time being; so, if we are to operate successful programs in this setting we must recognize the unfortunate image our official position evokes abroad and accept the political responsibilities that come with the program. It then becomes incumbent upon us to create programs with so much relevance, quality, and appeal that their success is assured even in this political milieu. It also behooves us to take the same great pains in their planning and administration that we do in the more obvious arenas of political and diplomatic intercourse. It is naïve indeed to acknowledge in principle that medical programs are perceived through a politico-diplomatic prism, but to plan, develop, and implement them as if they constituted a pure, uncomplicated scientific venture—and then expect them to be successful. As with programs of the highest political and diplomatic priority, a successful medical-assistance project must be based on research in depth that not only provides a theoretical knowledge of the proposed program but that also assures its practical relevance and adaptability to the foreign clime. The details of implementing the program must also reflect these political and diplomatic considerations.

The overriding principle in medical assistance to emerging nations is to create, develop, and administer programs that satisfy a priority *need* of the recipient, bringing to bear the particular skills which the donor possesses. The determination of that priority need must rest ultimately with the recipient, for only he knows what his priorities are at a given time and only he can assess the full gamut of factors that must influence his judgment.

On the other hand, of course, the donor and other international authorities can *assist* the recipient in arriving at its priorities. The donor might make available modern technological approaches to research and fact-finding, or he might lend personnel to work in concert with indigenous experts to help them put the issues into better focus. For example, according to all significant parameters, medical assistance to emerging countries should take the form of preventive rather than curative medical programs, although this concept still presents problems both at home and abroad. A donor who is asked to advise on an issue can only negotiate: if he fails in negotiation, he fails, and that is part of the game, for the ultimate judgment on needs and priorities must rest with the emerging country.

I am reminded of an incident that occured in India about two years ago. India, a huge area of endemic smallpox, was in the upswing of its epidemic curve for this disease when the program director was informed that the stock of smallpox vaccine was rapidly becoming depleted. India, accordingly, made a request to the World Health Organization for 10 million doses of multiple pressure vaccine to be administered by the traditional method of scarification. WHO passed the request on to the United States government, and from there it went to the National Communicable Disease Center in Atlanta, Ga. All of us in the smallpox program, both at headquarters in Atlanta and in the field were delighted with the request. Here at last was a chance to help India solve its smallpox problem with the mass vaccination techniques which had proved so effective in West Africa: by use of the jet-injector, an instrument capable of vaccinating 1,000 people an hour. The response to the request for 10 million doses of multiple pressure vaccine was given, then, with 10 million doses of *jet-injector* vaccine (and the promise of more to come), 50 jet-injectors, and two epidemiologists to advise on mass programs and train personnel in use of the jet-injector.

The epidemiologists arrived with all their gear, began training people, and mounted pilot projects to demonstrate the efficacy of the injector and their techniques. Finally they were ready for the mass campaign to begin. But nothing happened. Meeting after endless meeting, one fruitless conference after another occurred until it became patently clear that the Ministry of Health had no intention of mounting the type of campaign envisaged by the visitors. Confused and frustrated, the epidemiologists were moved to ask at a meeting what the problem was. An official of the ministry replied with a rhetorical question that demonstrated how completely the needs and desires of the recipient nation had been neglected in the enthusiasm of the donor. He responded most politely, "Gentlemen, if someone gave you an elephant as a sign of friendship, what would you say?"

The skills offered by the donor must not only be oriented toward the recipient's concept of its needs but must also reflect the specific characteristics of the country involved—its cultural attitudes, logistics, geography, climate, systems of administrations, and its economic and human resources. These differences among countries and peoples often make it impossible to mount a program in country *Y*, even when it has worked effectively in country *X*. If medical-assistance programs are to be planned carefully, well developed, and efficiently administered, they must be formulated not only on the basis of the solid theoretical knowledge available on the subject but also on appropriate prior homework for each program site.

A true story is told about a physician who became alarmed over his inability to keep a generator-driven freezer at optimal levels to preserve the heat-labile vaccine he was administering. The man cabled his headquarters base for advice and the answer came by return cable: he was advised to park his truck under a tree, where the temperature would be a few degrees cooler—not an unreasonable answer if he were working in a park, but distinctly inappropriate for a physician working in a sub-Saharan country on the fringes of the desert in an ambient temperature of 120 degrees. This example underscores the value of doing the proper homework, and that, before the fact.

It is also important both in negotiating programs and in implementing them to take into consideration the growing nationalism in the newly independent countries. Implicit here is an awareness of the sensitivities one can expect to encounter at all levels of activity. These nations are just now developing their technology, to be sure, but they have a culture which has been fully developed for centuries and of which they are justifiably proud. It is often difficult for some who have ben indoctrinated into thinking of these areas as the "underdeveloped" world to recognize that they have *anything* of value to offer or to be taken into account when programs are being developed there.

It is certainly in the interest of the donor country to see that its medical assistance has a unique appeal for the host country and is perceived in as favorable a light as possible. And it is in the interest of the recipient country for assistance to be delivered as efficiently as possible. These are not incompatible interests!

With competent leadership it is easy to make a basically good program successful. On the other hand, even with genius at the helm, it is impossible to sustain one badly conceived.

The success of the nineteen-country program for the eradication of smallpox illustrates the effectiveness of giving full consideration to the factors we have discussed. First, the program was designed to respond to a long-standing medical priority in many of these West African countries, and this need had been enunciated for a long time by the World Health Organization as well as by the involved countries. Smallpox has been a scourge to many communities, killing and maiming countless thousands for generations. In 1965 the World Health Organization reaffirmed an earlier unsuccessful position it had taken on global eradication, but this time the assembly requested that its more affluent member states provide bilateral assistance to those countries in which smallpox was endemic. In immediate response to this request, the government of the United States committed itself to work with other interested countries in eradicating the disease and agreed to take the original nineteen contiguous sub-Saharan countries of West Africa as its responsibility. The Agency for International Development delegated the responsibility for vaccinating 120 million people in an area larger than the United States itself to the National Communicable Disease Center in Atlanta. The center then set out to plan and develop this program.

I recall that active planning for this program began more than a year before the first American advisor departed for his assigned country. I recall that American experts were in the field visiting each of the nineteen countries a year before the American teams arrived in order to familiarize themselves with all the practical data necessary for complete and efficient planning. I also recall that 10 months before the American teams arrived in Africa, the National Communicable Disease Center convened an expert committee on the subject "Smallpox Eradication in a Developing Country"—a group made up of professionals from all over the world who assisted in planning the technical aspects of the program. I recall our scouring the nation to find Americans with first-hand knowledge of modern Africa to recruit some of the finest young men and young women in our land who would serve either as physician-epidemiologists or as public-health administrators and who would be the program's envoys and resident advisors in each country. These men and women were carefully selected not only for their expertise in epidemiology, disease control, and public-health practices but also with specific regard to their motivations and general suitability for the envisioned African experience. Further, the health workers were given a 10-week course before departure that covered not only the technical aspects of the program but also every recognizable discipline that might prove advantageous to their advisory function: culture, geography, politics, and economy plus extended training in the official language of the country to which they were to be assigned.

Unfortunately, however, the principles underlying this program represent the exception, not the rule. Too many medical programs theoretically designed to assist emerging countries are in fact developed around the needs or priorities of the donor country or, to put it in truly colonial terms, are based on what the donor country *believes* the needs of the recipient country are or should be. Even when overriding evidence indicates that the needs identified by the donor nation are valid, it is in my view a crass error—and, indeed, an inappropriate assumption of prerogatives—for a donor nation to attempt to force acceptance of medical programs on emerging countries. If we foist a medical principle upon an emerging country by threatening to withhold all other assistance unless the country complies, we must stand guilty of the worst kind of political intrigue; and under these circumstances we can forget whatever remains of the humane principles underlying the medical assistance offered.

Because of the growing crescendo of utterances on population control, I am constrained to present this as a pressing example. There is a suggestion that the Federal Government may well withhold all types of assistance from countries which fail to subscribe to modern concepts of population control and which do not set out to implement them. Equally deplorable is the suggestion attributed to a spokesman for the World Bank that all future development loans to emerging countries may be contingent upon the adoption of population-control programs. In addition, there are the unconscionable expressions of some experts who would have our government put sterility drugs in reservoirs and in food shipped to foreign countries in order to limit human multiplication.[1]

Many ongoing health programs that are saving lives daily in emerging countries are already in jeopardy of being curtailed or eliminated because of the cutbacks in foreign aid and foreign spending by the United States and other countries, and also because of the presently inadequate funding of the World Health Organization.[2] To limit these programs even further by attaching a population-control prerequisite is completely unjustifiable in humanitarian or ethical terms.

How do the potential recipients of population-control assistance view this issue? Specifically, in most of sub-Saharan Africa, promotion of population-control measures is perceived by many indigenous health authorities and statesmen as a subtle but hostile attempt to limit the power of these countries. These officials firmly believe they need *more* people, not less, in order to become viable nations. This position is more understandable when one recalls that in 1967 a South African "expert" recommended compulsory birth control for black Rhodesians and birth promotion with incentives for whites!

And in fact this problem of interpretation is by no means limited to the African continent. In travels around the country attending meetings and seminars on urban and community health —in San Francisco, in New York, in Los Angeles, in Boston— one hears loud outcries from ghetto residents expressing their distaste and suspicion of family-planning programs as separate activities, when there are so many inequities and gaps existing in the more conventional health services. It behooves us, then, not only to listen, but to heed!

And, indeed, in West Africa several objective factors lend support to the opposition of inhabitants to population-control measures. First, in terms of population distribution, West Africa is relatively under-populated. Second, as we have already noted, the mortality rate for children in the emerging countries is exceptionally high. Everyone has a basic right to "immortality," and in affluent societies the probability of achieving it exists through many mechanisms. For the desperately poor farmer in Ghana or Mali, however, his only hope for such immortality lies with his descendants, and I am concerned that we weigh this consideration so lightly.

Third, since West Africa lacks formal governmental systems for welfare and old-age assistance, children represent the only form of social security that aging parents have. The extended-family system common throughout West Africa represents more than a familial sharing of benefits and misfortunes: it means that whatever belongs to one member of the family becomes the property of the whole family, so that old age accompanied by the growth and production of many children and grandchildren is eagerly anticipated, not dreaded, as contrasted with our more impersonal social system. There are myriad factors governing human multiplication, and all these factors must be taken into consideration.

So, I submit, we must show parents in these emerging countries that their children can survive to adulthood, show them the fullness of life through health, education, and economic development, and they will limit their own families. The educated and affluent African knows what family planning is all about. But he represents only about 2 percent of the population, and this proportion must be increased enormously before the posture of the population-control experts can become comprehensible—or even tenable.

In summarizing this particular issue, let me add that there are strong, logical arguments which clearly indicate the wisdom of population control, and with these I have no contention. This issue, however, is so provocative and so emotionally charged that under no circumstance should acceptance of family-planning measures be stipulated as a prerequisite for anything—certainly not for desperately needed programs of foreign assistance! Such an approach is not only likely to be rejected itself but would also reduce receptivity to other more rational approaches—and half a loaf is better than none.

Instead of single-thrust or forced population-control measures, foreign assistance in medicine should be offered through a comprehensive, integrated program focusing on the total family. It should provide ongoing assistance in preventive public-health measures, health education, home economics, and sanitation, along with complete family-planning programs which should address themselves to the problems of subfertility as well. When these public-health programs are available in concert with traditional foreign assistance in education, agricultural development, and industrial development—all within a comprehensive foreign-aid philosophy—the ethics of birth control will become academic for many, and acceptance or rejection as a principle will lie where it belongs: with the individual, according to his own personal values.

Beyond satisfying a priority need in a recipient country, the basic justification for foreign medical assistance, it seems to me, is the building and development of institutions and the training of personnel, both planned so they can be expanded or modified to accommodate the delivery of other health programs at a future time. Programs planned and developed without heed to this underlying goal, no matter how well meant, how prestigious, or how glamorous, represent a luxury that developing countries can ill afford and beg the question of total national development in an emerging country.

In the West African program for the eradication of smallpox, fewer than 50 American trainer-advisors participated in the development of more than 4,000 indigenous Africans who learned to function in all program disciplines and at every level of supervision, based on their specific talents and experience. The African personnel actually carried out the smallpox program—a system that provided at least three rewards:

1. It developed a multidisciplined cadre of health workers specifically trained in the skills necessary to carry out their own duties; moreover, these workers were exposed to a complex program that allowed them to appreciate the relation of their contribution to the many other disciplines involved in the total effort.

2. These health workers developed the pride in accomplishment that is so necessary to continued involvement, morale, and fulfillment.

3. The institutions developed and the skills learned by the personnel can be modified to meet the delivery of other health services for the nation. For example, all these countries now have a built-in mechanism for responding to epidemics in the future or, more routinely, they can deliver other immunizations, as for polio, tetanus, and yellow fever. And with appropriate retraining these teams could effectively tackle the delivery of altogether different health services.

One final consideration seems essential in discussing how to make programs for foreign medical assistance more attractive and useful to the emerging countries. The developing countries in which I have had experience have created or are creating "development plans" for five-year periods. Some countries have already consummated their five-year plans and now have ten-year development plans in operation. These development plans, unique for each country, are created within a system that establishes priorities, coordinates related activities and programs, and reconciles the envisioned programs with available manpower and budgetary determinations. These plans are predicted to some extent, of course, on certain expectations of foreign assistance from given sources.

These long-term guidelines and priorities in the emerging countries would seem to offer an excellent opportunity for coordinated multiple donor-nation activity. If each nation would coordinate its contribution with those of other donors, measurable portions of the five- and ten-year plans could be expedited from year to year in an orderly fashion. Unfortunately, since donor nations regard their assistance programs to emerging countries as private preserves, as tools of political strategy, each seeks to develop so complete a package that the recipient cannot possibly resist. This would be the best of all possible worlds if the recipient nation could actually accept all the packages offered. Paradoxically, however, one important factor prevents this: the recipient country's own lack of resources, both human and financial.

I am reminded of a provocative suggestion made by a ranking official of the Ministry of Health in The Gambia, that tiny slip of a country placed on the shores of the Gambia River with a population of about 285,000. When asked at an early stage why The Gambia was making progress so slowly in the organization and planning of its smallpox program, he replied, "Why don't you donor countries and agencies get together and coordinate your offers of assistance in health programs instead of coming to us individually with something new and attractive? Our needs are so great that we can use almost any sort of assistance in health programs, but our personnel and financial resources are so limited that developing a new program frequently means removing personnel from other programs." The *pièce de résistance* was his statement, "We don't dare turn you down for fear that you'll become provoked, and then you may not make us another offer for several years."

A look at one small coastal West African country of 2.3 million inhabitants amply illustrates this point. No fewer than nine Western nations supply assistance to this country for health programs, agricultural and industrial development, and education. The support is channeled through 12 independent projects which are totally uncoordinated—even within the health field itself. This lack of coordination among the donors has forced the recipient government to shift priorities, rotate civil servants from project to project, and juggle the budget of the realm to meet its commitments to each foreign donor.

As a result of this uncoordinated donor activity, the ministries of health in emerging countries find themselves embroiled in foreign-assistance programs which are begun and abandoned or are staggering along with no hope of successful conclusion, programs which represent scattered thrusts in terms of meeting the total needs, and programs which at best overlap and frequently duplicate effort. Clearly this situation is a luxury that none can afford.

I have tried to present some of the influences and observations that have surfaced during my active participation in official American medical programs and from my exposure to others in developing countries. I should like to summarize these as follows:

The gap between the ideal and the real relation between medicine and diplomacy has been examined at some length. While I share the view of many that, ideally, these disciplines should provide a unique and effective resource for the delivery of health assistance to emerging countries, the fact is that they do not. I have suggested, then, some influences that must be taken into account if we are to overcome this unfortunate situation

It has been pointed out that infectious diseases and malnutrition in childhood pose the greatest threat to life in the developing countries, and evidence has been given to support the overwhelming mortality rate among children in these countries as contrasted with our own. The desperate need for assistance, then, is there.

The importance of the donor's satisfying a priority need of the recipient has been emphasized and it has been stressed that the determination of that need must, in the final analysis, rest with the recipient.

A related tenet is that in responding with the required skills to recipient-set priorities, the donor country must do its homework before developing programs—taking full account of all the vagaries that may exist in a given program site.

I have deplored the blackmail implicit in making foreign medical assistance contingent upon anything and have made a special issue of population control, which looms as the most forbidding example in this context. I have suggested a reasonable alternative to this all or nothing approach.

It has been stated that the most important philosophy in the development of medical programs in emerging countries must be the building of institutions and the training of skilled personnel— both capable of adaptation to the delivery of other health efforts in the future.

The increasing reliance of the emerging nations on five- and ten-year development plans was suggested as an excellent opportunity for donor nations to coordinate their programs of medical assistance. Such a coordination of health assistance would avoid duplication and wasted efforts and, most important, would allow the recipient nations to deploy their limited personnel and financial resources far more more efficiently than at present.

Finally, if we really cared, we could and should rethink and restructure our entire administrative mechanism for delivering programs of medical assistance to developing countries. We could sacrifice the need to maintain and promote our national image for the fulfillment of the need in developing countries for improved health conditions; and we could let the virtue of providing medical assistance to those who desperately need it be its own reward—if we really cared!

Notes

1. Paul Erlich, Ph.D., at the U.S. National Commission for UNESCO Biennial Conference, "Man and His Environment," November 23 to 25, 1969, San Francisco. Quoted in the *New York Times,* November 24, 1969.
2. See, for example, R. W. Apple, Jr., "Vital Foreign Aid Drying up in Black Africa," *New York Times,* November 24, 1969.

A War We *Can* Win

Health as a Vector of Foreign Policy

Hugh L. Carey

I T IS TIME our country won a war. In my lifetime I have fought in one war and helped to finance four others, and I have not felt like a winner yet. In the past 50 years more than a million American casualties and the expenditure of trillions of dollars have not secured peace on earth.

In the 1970's, for a change, I should like to see us enter a war we can win. Let me suggest a winning strategy for the war of the 1970's: first, we should pick an old opponent already on the downgrade: man's most ancient enemy—disease and its allies, hunger and ignorance. Next, enlist the largest possible army—all mankind—in a common and united front to wage an all-out assault on an aggressor who respects no borders: premature death. For leadership we should seek the ministers of the healing arts, those whose efforts are in the style of Albert Schweitzer, of Thomas A. Dooley, of Father Damien and of Jonas Salk. A foreign-policy effort that would utilize medicine and health care has proved its soundness in the past. It would justify a new initiative in the 1970's.

The horror of November 1970 in the Bay of Bengal makes such a new initiative compelling if we are to preserve our heritage as a compassionate people.

One hundred and fifty thousand men, women, and children died; cholera, famine, and pestilence spread, and the world, without and within our own country, gazed on with seeming indifference.

It is true that the administration released $10 million (of a contingency and catastrophe fund of over $700 million; a citizens' committee was appointed, and eight or ten helicopters were crated and shipped to be manned by one or two platoons of infantry from Fort Bragg.

But where was the facility, the technical, medical, health, and nutritional team to move in and save some of those 150,000 casualties or the next 150,000, who will also die without the help which we among all nations are the most able to extend.

Is it possible that we as a people are developing a "Genovese" syndrome? (Kitty Genovese was assaulted and brutally murdered in a middle-class neighborhood in New York while a score of onlookers roused by her cries failed to intervene or call for help.)

Helmut Sorge, the Washington bureau chief of *Der Spiegel* wrote in a tone of outrage to the *Washington Post* as follows:

> Has the world lost the capacity for sorrow, has it lost the ability to be shocked, have the gas chambers of Auschwitz, have Hiroshima, the French carnage in Algeria, the destruction of Vietnam by the missionaries of "God's own country" amputated the world's conscience?
>
> How, one wonders, would the world react if 150,000 white men had been washed into the ocean on the coast of Holland, if cholera threatened to destroy the nation of tulip-growers—how the world would groan over the terrible loss! But whether black or yellow, whether they are Indians in the refuges of the nation, or the starving populations of northern Brazil, they do not count in an already over-populated world, they are insignificant in the eyes of the white

world, marginally productive, useless for the construction of the capitalist pyramids.

When four people are murdered in California, what a drama unfolds in the name of humanity, how decent we are, how humane we are, we even give every human being a fair chance.

The world does not seem to have any standards for humanity anymore. A man possesses human dignity only insofar as other men confer it upon him. If he lives in Pakistan he is a sub-human, if he lives in Biafra he is only a bushman, dying unnoticed like the wild animals. The death of 150,000 humans in Pakistan, brown-skinned and thousands of miles away, is evidently no loss for our civilization; "That's the way it is," say the Walter Cronkites and then we switch once more to consumer advertisements and aspirin commercials, the best remedy against the headaches of this world. A healthy, human world.[1]

The *Washington Post* responded to the Sorge letter in an editorial entitled "Passing By on the Other Side."[2]

. . . Dacca is so far away and so little a part of *our* world that the death of a couple of hundred thousand or even a million Pakistanis seems no concern of ours. Man's compassion for the rest of humanity has been blunted by the disasters, man-made as well as natural, that have swept the world in our lifetimes. It is easy now, easier than it might have been in calmer days early in this century, to brush aside the reports of 168,000 known dead and unknown thousands more missing or dying as one of those things that happens. And this brutal process of brushing aside becomes even easier as general knowledge of the world's population problem spreads.

. . . None of this, of course, excuses the Pharisee-like attitude most of the world has taken toward the survivors of the Ganges River disaster. Most of the news media, ourselves included, have treated it as just another chapter, and a brief one at that in the tragedies that have befallen mankind. The government of Pakistan was unbelievably slow in beginning relief operations and in using the materials made available to it. The other governments, our own included, have hung back presumably waiting for the Pakistanis to lay claim on their services. Meanwhile, people have continued to die, from disease and starvation if not from the water and the wind. It has been a sad demonstration, not only of man's inability to control or predict the disaster that Nature can unleash but also of his decreasing ability to be compassionate toward his fellow men.

Whether one agrees with Sorge in part or at all it cannot be denied that we could do more than we are now doing to prevent diseases, famine, and catastrophe in the world.

In fact, a review of our own history will show that when we had less we did more proportionately. When we were not so strong we were more generous to the weak. When we were less well fed, we helped others fend off famine.

A review of the rhetoric of our country's leadership will show that our compassion has long been stated; now it needs to be demonstrated and implemented.

The Historical Basis

Every time we have supported medical leadership in international health we have won battle after battle and inflicted all the casualties among the insects and microscopic organisms which prey upon man and the other animals.

Medical leadership and foreign policy are not new companions. We are indebted to Dr. Kevin M. Cahill, the editor of this book, for an excellent review of the role of medicine in international diplomacy. In his report "Medicine and Diplomacy in the Tropics,"[3] Dr. Cahill traces the history of the humanitarian alliance of health and statecraft. He tells us that six of the signers of the Declaration of Independence were physicians and that the last president of the Republic of Texas was a doctor. He identifies leaders in other lands as physicians: Georges Clemenceau in France; Isidro Ayora in Ecuador; Juscalino Kubitschek in Brazil; and H. Kamuza Banda in Malawi. Representative Thomas E. Morgan of Pennsylvania, chairman of the Committee on Foreign Affairs in the House of Representatives, is a practicing physician. It would be an error to depict the doctor in diplomacy as a practitioner in rhetoric or a surgeon in striped pants: in reality he is a pioneer.

Historically, American medical help has been used to open new frontiers in our hemisphere and around the world. Significantly, our major efforts to employ overseas health care as a measure of our national interest have in many cases followed the end of military operations. In 1798, in postrevolutionary America, President John Adams signed the law to establish the Marine Hospital, which became our U.S. Public Health Service. One hundred years later, in 1899, after the Spanish-American War, Walter Reed led the U.S. Army Yellow Fever Commission in the assault on yellow fever in the Caribbean and, by 1901, the disease had been completely eradicated in Havana. The construction of the Panama Canal was made possible through the program led by Dr. William Crawford Gorgas. Sixty years later in Havana, American medicine came to the rescue of our foreign policy after the abortive mishap of the Bay of Pigs, Cuba: 1,700 prisoners were released and Cuba received $25 million worth of drugs supplied by American firms through the Pharmaceutical Manufacturers' Association as a result of adroit negotiations conducted by Attorney General Robert F. Kennedy and the late James B. Donovan.

In wartime I witnessed how Europeans esteemed Dwight D. Eisenhower, our commanding general, and President Franklin D. Roosevelt for their leadership in liberation. But Herbert Hoover was revered as well for his mission after World War I that had supplied food, medicine, and other necessities to millions of victims of that war.

However, it was Harry S. Truman, our postwar president in

1949, who set forth with historic determination the humanitarian commitment as it is, or should be, today.

The Foreign Policy Pathmark

In his Inaugural Address, 1949, President Truman stated:

> For the first time in history, humanity possesses the knowledge and the skill to relieve the suffering of these people.
>
> The United States is pre-eminent among nations in the development of industrial and scientific techniques. The material resources which we can afford to use for the assistance of other peoples are limited. But our imponderable resources in technical knowledge are constantly growing and are inexhaustible.
>
> I believe that we should make available to peace-loving peoples the benefits of our store of technical knowledge in order to help them realize their aspirations for a better life.[4]

This policy became the Marshall Plan, which has had no equal as an effective instrument in furthering American foreign policy. Much of its success was due to the fact that it incorporated extensive public-health programs that were made available to needy nations. Out of such efforts emerged the World Health Organization (WHO), which has served to at least identify vividly the needs of the health-poor peoples of the earth.

Because disease respects no boundaries, President John F. Kennedy emphasized in his foreign policy, through the Agency for International Development, the principle of interdependency of nations in health planning and operations.

Involved in a tragic war, President Lyndon B. Johnson saw that violence in and among nations results when suffering people lose confidence in their governments. This is particularly true in small nations but it is becoming painfully evident now in great powers also. Speaking as the leader of the world's greatest power in 1966 he called for action in international health and education in his message to Congress:

We have committed ourselves for many years to relieving human suffering. Today our effort must keep pace with a growing world and with growing problems. Therefore, I propose a program to create an international career service in health; help meet health manpower needs in developing nations; combat malnutrition; control and eradicate disease; co-operate in world-wide efforts to deal with population problems.[5]

The president had reason to feel that his words fell on sympathetic ears. Congress has been saying for years in the language of the Foreign Assistance Act: "Ignorance, want, and despair breed extremism and violence which lead to aggression and violence."

It is sad to relate today that the International Health Education Act, calling for an expenditure of only $10 million, died in the Rules Committee in 1966 and has yet to be resurrected. This happened despite the fact that John Gardner, then Secretary of Health, Education, and Welfare, had said before the Congressional committee which considered this bill:

> One of the necessities of our time is to create the kind of relationships with other countries which will enable all of us to live in peace. More than ever befoie, all of us recognize that the hazard of war is greater than any other.
>
> There may be many ways to reduce this hazard, but there are few which are better than establishing constructive working relationships in those fields of human endeavor in which all men share the same aims, the same hopes, the same goals. Health is such a field. There are no better grounds on which we can meet other nations and demonstrate our own concern for peace and the betterment of mankind than in a common battle against disease.
>
> To this field, we can bring special competence, we can address ourselves to the alleviation of serious but soluble problems. We can relate ourselves constructively to others in improving international understanding and co-operation.
>
> Furthermore, when we engage in such shared work with

the health professions in other lands, particularly in the developing nations, we are relating ourselves to key groups and individuals, destined to play vitally important roles in shaping the future of their countries.

It is important to note that any aid to improve the health of people in other countries—especially in the developing nations—will be a substantial contribution not only to their health status and their freedom from disease, but also to their educational status, their food production, their economic strength, their social stability, and the attainment of that level of social and economic development which will permit them to be self-sufficient and self-supporting.

We could bring these benefits to many nations simply by exporting our know-how, at relatively little cost to ourselves.[6]

Exporting Our Know-How: A Boon and a Bargain

"Exporting our know-how, at relatively little cost to ourselves"—this would seem to be the kind of boon at bargain price which should appeal to even the most cost-conscious Congress. The 89th Congress, however, was not convinced even though the Committee, in favorably reporting the bill, stated that this would mobilize slightly less than 1 per cent of America's total health-manpower pool.

With unusual Congressional chagrin the Committee further stated:

> It will be noted that this number (of trainees) is considerably less than the number of M.D.'s licensed in the U.S. which is draining scarce medical manpower from other nations in the world for our domestic health problems.[7]

On this same point, in an address titled "Medicine: The Global Diplomat," former Secretary of State Dean Rusk pointed out how we are "sopping up" medical talent from developing countries. Mr. Rusk stated.

> Now, if there is a country which can produce its own resources for its own medical care, surely it must be the

United States. For if we cannot do it, who can? And if we get in a position of absorbing from countries who are in desperate need of their talents and their manpower, then we have some very major problems in front of us.[8]

The unfortunate history of this legislation serves to illustrate that Congress is not moving to win this war that we can win against disease and premature death. What is even more tragic is that in this hour, in the most productive period in the history of this or any other nation, we propose to do even less in the years ahead. Our arsenal of aid in the war we can win in health is provided basically in the Foreign Assistance Act. Under this we provide for our cooperation in the World Health Organization, our aid to developing nations for the needs in health and sanitation, and our programs to cope with the crisis in population.

The record of recent months shows a unilateral withdrawal—a retreat from man's most ancient and newly vulnerable enemy: disease. Since 1948 and the Marshall Plan, Congress has appropriated about $47 billion for foreign assistance. As a percentage of our gross national product this equaled 2 per cent in 1949; declined to two thirds of 1 per cent in 1954; and one half of 1 per cent in 1962. The $1.6 billion proposed by Congress in the pending appropriation for fiscal year 1970 is less than one fourth of 1 per cent of our $800 billion of the total production of the United States. In our effort, as compared with that of other industrial nations who provide assistance in development to our weaker neighbors, the United States has fallen from first to eighth place.

I recently asked a representative of the Agency for International Development (AID): "At what point does this program become marginally effective in terms of being funded at levels too low to have significant impact?" He answered, "I believe we may have passed that point two years ago."

Recognizing the status of Congressional antipathy to universal technical-assistance programs and the failure of the present administration to exercise leadership as yet in this field, is it realistic to talk of a new initiative in world health on the part of the United States?

Is a New Initiative Feasible?

My answer is that it will take some hard selling, but I consider it possible to convince Congress that health care is an effective instrument of foreign policy in at least four ways:

First, I submit that health care is our lowest-cost form of international security and protection against war and violence. In a recent eight-year period, 87 per cent of the very poor nations, 69 per cent of the poor nations, 48 per cent of the middle-income nations, and just 4 per cent of the rich nations experienced insurrection or aggression.[9] The recent overthrow of governments in developing and less-developed countries proves that the smaller nations are a long way from stability and that disorders in their countries tend to bring the great powers into conflict on one side or the other. In recent months Peru, Ecuador, and Panama have erupted, to say nothing of Nigeria, Biafra, Libya, Dahomey, and Guinea.

Corpsman to Mankind, Not Policeman of the World

As we watch these seemingly superficial eruptions on the various continents we might well remember that great wars have started in backyard quarrels. Conflict among remote neighbors in the Balkans, in the Ruhr and Saar valleys, and in Vietnam eventually involved the United States. It is true that we became involved under the notion that we had a function as policeman of the world. It is apparent from the statements of the Nixon administration and of many Congressional leaders that we no longer regard ourselves as such even though we carry the "biggest stick" in history, referred to by the administration as our "nuclear umbrella." The difficulty, of course, is that there are also sticks of similar if not equal weight in other hands so that we cannot afford the least instability in smaller nations lest that instability trigger the ultimate nuclear destruction.

If our country is not to act as a policeman of the world and wield the bomb as a club, then perhaps in our own interest and in the interest of humanity we might consider ourselves as corpsman to mankind, bearing the balm of healing and helping. Exporting our know-how in health care at relatively little cost to ourselves should be an attractive alternative to some high-cost, low-yield programs of foreign aid that we now support under the name of mutual security.

For decades we have scattered our hardware among weakling autocracies, old colonial powers, and juntas passing through the palaces of developing nations as though they were swinging doors. From Sherman tanks to surplus ships we have dispensed so-called defensive weapons to nations we have described as our eligible friends.

All too often, unfortunately, these weapons have been used to sustain governments which must perpetuate themselves in power through the force of "borrowed" arms. Such governments must use arms to promote stability through force because they have failed to win the loyalty and support of their people. I believe it would be worth our effort to see if the ill and starving people of the weak nations would prefer a ton of food or a kilo of vaccine to a ton of ammunition.

An American Corpsman Health Program could aid any government interested in the preservation of life in its own country; this could also be done on a regional basis.

It is not an abstraction that health programs can promote stability and protect against chronic anarchy.

Health as an Instrument of Stability

Herbert Singer, chairman of the board of the World Health Foundation, has discussed "Health as an Instrument of Foreign Policy." He pointed out: "Health and health programs have a unique capacity to touch the lives of individuals and families and to do so more dramatically than perhaps any other service of government."

Mr. Singer cites the following examples, which I believe are persuasive:

In Colombia where guerrilla warfare has had, for years, fertile territory within which to function, health has recently taken on a new and significant role. A successful program is now in operation by the Colombian Navy which, in addition to its prime mission of policing the Magdalena River, has added a medical and dental service for an area previously deemed isolated and unfriendly to the military. This health program, built around the gun boat and rendering service to people living within range of the river, has changed the image of Navy personnel in that territory from that of enemy to that of friend. It has produced vital intelligence of the hinterland of the river never before known or understood. In bringing the people of the area into league with the Navy, it has generated an extraordinary loyalty to the government in a vast area previously deemed, at the very least, unfriendly. The program has been so successful that a new vessel is now being completed to bring the program to the head waters of the Amazon River on the other side of the Andes.[10]

It is not accidental that the Feldsher System of medicine was incorporated in the Soviet health system in the very early days of their revolution and has been built upon vigorously ever since. To provide a broad and immediate base of medicine for the people of the Soviet Union, the Feldsher System provides medical coverage to a community, not through graduate doctors, but through specially trained personnel to deal, on a personal level, with a limited scope of medical needs. The system may not produce the highest quality of medicine, but it has permitted the Soviet government to give to the masses of its people, broad, immediate, and effective health coverage. It is said that the Soviet people consider their medical system one of the fundamentally important dividends from their government.

It is interesting to note that, at a recent conference of the Pan American Health Organization in Trinidad, the Cuban delegation wished to dramatize its health program (which follows the Soviet system) and requested a comparative examination of health programs in Latin America. This request was for the obvious purpose of demonstrating Cuba's superior coverage of its people's health needs as against the relatively low health coverage of the "imperialistic" oriented governments of Latin America. Castro, very early in his regime, endeavored to dramatize to his people his concern for their health: and it is not all surprising that Castro insisted on drugs and medical supplies as a major consideration for his release of prisoners captured in the Bay of Pigs incident. It is particularly interesting to note that Castro is presently using the Cuban health structure and personnel as a means of communicating with his people on a political as well as a health level.

Negatively, we have seen the strong reaction of people when a government health service is withdrawn or curtailed, as took place in England and in other countries in recent years.

The horror of our experience in Vietnam should teach Congress something about the present instability of small governments. The Thieu regime there is the latest administration in a series which sought to win the loyalty of its citizens by both democratic and undemocratic means.

In Vietnam, experience shows that one of our most successful efforts in pacification has been in the field of health services. There is another lesson for us. We have spent as much on Vietnam— $120 billion—as we have on the entire Foreign Assistance Program since it began 21 years ago!

The second way in which Congress may be sold on health is to point out that a new priority program which has found favor with the White House and Congress—population control—may be ineffective without companion programs in public health. This will be particularly true in the poorest nations with the highest birthrates unless we also promote or help to provide a system for the delivery of health services that include maternity, child health, and nutrition as integral to family planning.

This we have not done. Instead, in order to underwrite a new national and international emphasis in family planning, Congress has earmarked a rising level of funds for family planning while decreasing the level of technical assistance, which includes health services. As a result, little assistance is now available for the improvement of the basic structures of developing countries for providing health services at the local level.

In Africa, in fiscal year 1968, 80 per cent of all the AID funds available for health, population, and nutrition were allocated to just two projects: the Regional Measles Control–Smallpox Eradication Project that serves nineteen countries and the Ibadan Water Supply Project in Nigeria.

No amount of money for family planning will have the desired effect on fertility rates, disease, or nutrition until we achieve some simple way of handling all three.

Notestein, Kirk, and Segal in 1963 observed: "No efforts of socio-economic development can be successful in a disease-ridden population, nor will a desire for small families be likely to emerge. Better health and improved chances for survival of the individual child lie at the root of the motivational change we are seeking."[11]

Dr. Walsh McDermott agrees with Barbara Ward,[12] the economist, that the population question has "suffered badly from misleading simplifications. The very broad generalization is true, however, that as long as there continues a high infant and early childhood mortality it is very hard to make sustained high fertility seem disadvantageous. Thus the high early mortality blocks creation of the preconditions necessary for reduction in fertility that is, in itself, necessary for reduction of early mortality."[13]

Population control as an element of our foreign policy in health, then, if it is to succeed, turns on the readiness of Congress and the President to support the development of a new system of health-care delivery adaptable to the traditional societies in the underdeveloped countries.

To be adaptable such a system need not and should not be the kind of sophisticated system common to Western civilization. Our highly developed health system is outstripping our means so fast that it is obviously too costly to export all over the world.

Further, it is of little use in the treatment of illiterate patients who know neither when they were born nor how old they are in terms of our years or who must observe local taboos by sticking pins in a doll to describe their symptoms or must communicate their aches and pains in West Nigeria through the *dokita* (native doctor), the *babalawos* (Ifa priests), or the *oniseguns* (herbalists).

Since our American system of health care is too advanced in practice and in cost to be feasible for use in the developing countries, how are we to export our know-how in health care? The answer is neither to ignore the challenge nor the opportunity to serve mankind but to adapt ourselves to the varieties of need.

When President John F. Kennedy saw the need for a new instrument for technical assistance to the developing nations he did not conscript the graduate schools at the Massachusetts Institute of Technology, at the California Institute of Technology, or at the Georgetown School of Foreign Service. Rather he founded the Peace Corps as a broadly based agency for voluntary service tailored to interface the needs of the host country with the talents of American volunteers.

Anyone who has priced our Peace Corps effort in cost-benefit terms will reach the conclusion that the return to our nation, to the host countries, and to the individuals involved has been profitable beyond measure.

On the basis of this record I suggest that a third way to persuade Congress and the administration to support a new initiative in this war we can win is that we should begin with an economical low-cost developmental project which would entail neither a vast financial nor skilled manpower commitment.

I urge, therefore, that the United States undertake the foundation of an International Health Corpsman Program. Such a program would be multilateral; it would involve both the personnel and resources of other willing nations in cooperation with but not under WHO.

I suggest the latter because of the presently limited resources of

WHO (approximately $100 million worldwide) as well as the political structures which bind WHO as an agency of the United Nations.

The program would be one of training and placement at the invitation of host countries in need of mobile medical and paramedical, technical, and subtechnical personnel, specifically trained for the needs of the area to be served.

Miss Julia Walsh, while a senior at New York University School of Medicine, attended the World Health Assembly as student representative. She describes such a plan in her excellent article, "Medical Education and World Health."[14] Miss Walsh suggests the need for measurements of productivity of health personnel and she says that "with the increasing use of labor-saving devices a health worker is able to serve more people or larger areas in a shorter time but first he must be skilled to use these devices." She further points out that the particular combination of medical and paramedical personnel to best meet the needs of the specific country and to use its resources most efficiently can be determined; this of course will differ in each instance. The educational system for the development of the health personnel requires variation suited to the particular country. The training plan, according to Miss Walsh, should take into account the nature of services to be provided and be tailored to fulfill the needs defined.

A nation which has learned to train technicians such as we have for space, for military purposes, for agriculture, etc., should have little difficulty in developing a versatile system of training medical and health personnel in such an effort. The advances we have made in programmed instruction, the available trained medical-corps personnel discharged from the armed forces, and the ability we have to train others by example are factors in our favor.

In fact it is precisely because we have the competence that I feel we have a moral as well as humanitarian imperative to undertake such a program. We have the know-how to prevent, to cure, to immunize, and we have done so on an isolated basis in the tropics, in the ghettos, in Appalachia, and in the war-ravaged areas of the world.

Not only have we the know-how but we have mastered the technique of mobility necessary for on-the-spot delivery of services as well as the needed support and communications vital to such a program. The world would benefit from our helicopters, field radios, massive airlift capacity, and all-round logistical competence gained in military activity.

It is no small coincidence that our system of national security and our leadership in international security will equip us to move from a post of policeman of the world to corpsman to humanity in need.

There are few legislators now in Congress who are as knowledgeable on health matters as our present Secretary of Defense and former Congressman Melvin Laird. Over many years in the House, as a member of the Subcommittee on Health, Education, and Welfare of the Appropriations Committee of the House of Representatives, he provided vital leadership, particularly in the support of research and international cooperation in health. How fitting it would be for us now to apply some of the savings we forecast in defense to a modest initiation in winning the war against disease. Defense of medical manpower resources could be of significant help in another way. We have scarce medical personnel "locked" into our Selective Service, a commissioned-medical-officer system to a greater degree than seems justifiable at this time. As of June 1969 in the Department of the Army, the branch with the highest rate of hospital patients, there were 32,000 inpatients. There were 7,132 Medical Corps officers on duty or approximately one doctor for every five patients. Armywide, among 1,500,000 personnel in uniform, the doctor-patient ratio is 4.72 per 1,000—or three times better than that among civilians.

Couple this with the fact that most doctors in the armed services are under a six-year obligation for two years of active duty during which their professional skills are usually devoted to a limited range of practice. The figures cited for the army alone, extended by the similar situations in the air force and navy, should provide some basis for a possible alternative as we move toward voluntary service in the armed forces. Such an alternative might well be for doctors to serve for a limited period in training and preparing the mobile medical and auxiliary units which would be the heart of this program. It need not be emphasized that the staffing of such units would provide an opportunity for young Americans who are seeking an alternative to serving in combat. Young people today are in search of unconventional careers. What I am suggesting is a radically different and unconventional approach to the practice of medicine. The medicine we know involves a doctor-patient ratio of 1:1,000. The ratio among foreign persons would be 1:20,000. Medical tasks which are fairly simple and occur frequently would devolve upon auxiliaries. Simple health centers, mobile units, and guided self-care could bring millions of lives into productive activity and turn the tide against death at infancy, death at adolescence, death from privation at any age.

As an original site for a training unit and staging area for movement into Asia and Africa, regions of need, we might consider Saipan, in the Mariana Islands, or other tropical sectors in the Trust Territory of the Pacific Islands under control of the United States. Our strategic trust agreement with the United Nations would permit this kind of activity and would in fact be of benefit to Micronesia.

We now have in Micronesia a health-training facility that turns out vocational-school-age male and female health assistants in nursing and allied health programs, almost all of whom will return to their native districts. In addition, in American Samoa we have the new Lyndon Johnson Tropical Disease Center, which could provide technical aid and research to such a facility. A similar undertaking in Puerto Rico or the Virgin Islands could be organized to serve Latin and South America.

It is apparent that we have the basic elements needed to originate this program without any vast new budgetary expenditure.

More effective support for present limited efforts to prevent disease would be one dividend from a better organized system.

Present Programs Could Be Improved

Such a system would serve as a multiplier of medical skills at low cost and would implement our present programs more effectively in all phases of health care from fertility control to treatment of infectious disease. With a clinical program such as this we could both accelerate and intensify not only the campaign against yellow fever and smallpox, but also against measles, scarlet fever, diphtheria, and all the other killing and crippling diseases we have eliminated in this country. As mentioned by Dr. Lythcott, one of the best coordinated and most successful foreign-assistance programs on record was completed in 1970: it freed 120 million people from smallpox in nineteen countries of West and Central Africa.

This is progress, but we know that more than half of all the children born in Africa die before the age of five. I asked an official of our AID program why we did not give multiple vaccinations at the same time for tetanus, diphtheria, typhoid, typhus, measles, scarlet fever, etc., as we do in this country. I was told that there was not enough money for the cost of the serum, even though these vaccines are the lowest-cost pharmaceuticals that money can buy. I have learned since that many American pharmaceutical houses such as Merck, Pfizer, SKF, etc., have donated much of these drugs. More could be used if we had a system of clinical inoculation. An additional fact that should appeal to Congress would be that American tourist taxpayers and traveling Congressmen now spend more than $20 million a year in getting immunization shots for overseas travel which they should not need if we could expedite our immunization and control program.

We Can Succeed

The fourth and last reason why a new and greater effort should be made to win the war against disease is that we can anticipate the kind of success factor that Congress and the administration seek in new programs.

We can expect success because of the example set for our government by private agencies which have proved their effectiveness under most trying conditions all over the world. Eighty-two American organizations under private auspices are working overseas alone or in cooperation with the Public Health Service, AID, the Peace Corps or branches of our Armed Forces Medical System. Care-Medico, the Dooley Foundation, Project Hope, the major religious groups—Catholic, Protestant, Jewish, and others —are the best emissaries of the United States we have in the world.

Here again, by more imaginative and innovative utilization of overseas diplomatic agencies, we could augment and assist the work of these organizations and individuals. Instead there are instances, as in Paraguay, where our policies actually hinder and hamper the efforts of voluntary missions working at the local level in the war against hunger and disease.

I advocate that the President use diplomatic efforts in aid of a war that we can win against disease in several other specific ways.

1. As we now do in the International Postal Agreement and the early-warning service of hurricanes and other meteorological phenomena, we can organize a network for world health in cooperation with all willing nations.

Such a communications system is now tied in to a limited degree with the Communicable Disease Center in Atlanta, Ga., which we use to alert us in our successful programs in Foreign Disaster Emergency Relief under AID. We know we can defeat and eliminate kwashiorkor or yaws or snail disease or tropical infections wherever they appear.

2. By international negotiation similar to the Geneva Convention in warfare, we can take the lead in freeing doctors and other health professionals from all restrictions to travel on professional

and health missions. It simply does not make sense to deny our health and medical skills to nations from whom we have withdrawn diplomatic recognition. The best way to get diplomacy going again would be to have our health scientists in constant communication with their colleagues throughout the world.

3. To broaden this understanding of health needs and opportunities I urge the Federal Government to assist educational institutions in studies in this field. The new institutes on campus for African, Asian, and Hispanic studies, for instance, could well help battle against disease in the developing countries.

No cause can prevail today unless it has earned the confidence and gained the support of young people. I believe the cause of international health and winning the war against disease is that kind of cause.

I am inspired, therefore, to see that the *New Physician,* the journal of the Student American Medical Association, in its issue of October 1969, devotes its entire issue to international health. That issue reveals the desire of young doctors and students who are working in remote and primitive corners of the world to better their skills and extend them to those most in need.

The editorial in this issue is eloquent:

> It is the two central aspects of medicine which have given it universal appeal as a humanitarian discipline. The first is its basic act, which is that of one human being helping another in need. The second is its basic method, which is science. The human crises of illness and death are universal, knowing no political, economic, or social boundaries, and science, in an age when advocacy silences dialogue and caps the ear of reason, is a last redoubt of a healthful cultural relativism, which sees mostly wonder in a fellow human's different way of life without a dimming veil of xenophobic arrogance.[15]

Our student doctors give us hope that in this century we can win our greatest conquest. In the nineteenth century Sir Ronald Ross prayed for help in his research to find the "unseen, small

million murderous killer"; we now pray for victory also, mindful
of his words:

> This day relenting God
>   Hath placed within my hand
> A wondrous thing. And God
>   Be praised, at his command
> Seeking his secret deeds,
>   With tears and toiling breath,
> I find thy cunning seeds,
>   O million-murdering death,
> I know this little thing
>   A myriad men will save,
> O death, where is thy sting?
>   Thy victory, O grave?

We can win the war against the unseen "million-murdering
killer."

It is a challenge to save our children and thus to serve our
creator and our country.

Notes

1. *Washington Post,* November 27, 1970.
2. *Ibid.*
3. K. M. Cahill, "Medicine and Diplomacy in the Tropics," *New York Journal of Medicine* 67 (1967) 2229-2238.
4. H. S. Truman, Inaugural Address, *Congressional Record,* January 20, 1949 (Washington: Government Printing Office, 1949), p. 447-448.
5. President Lyndon B. Johnson, Message to Congress on International Education and Health Acts, *Congressional Record,* Feburary 2, 1966 (Washington: Government Printing Office, 1966), pp. 1738-1741.
6. Hearing before the Committee on Interstate and Foreign

Commerce, House of Representatives, 89th Congress on H.R. 12453, International Health Act of 1966 (Washington: Government Printing Office, 1966), pp. 6-7.

7. House Report No. 1317, House of Representatives, 89th Congress, International Health Act of 1966 (Washington: Government Printing Office, 1966), p. 8.

8. D. Rusk, "Medicine: The Global Diplomat," Fourth Conference on International Health (American Medical Association), Chicago, Illinois, May 17-18, 1969. Unpublished.

9. R. S. McNamara, Address before the American Society of Newspaper Editors, Montreal, Canada, May 18, 1966. Unpublished.

10. H. M. Singer, "Health as an Instrument of Foreign Policy," *Congressional Record,* February 19, 1968, (Washington: Government Printing Office, 1968), p. E-870.

11. F. W. Notestein, D. Kirk, and S. Segal, "The Problem of Population Control," in P. M. Hauser, ed., *The Population Dilemma* (Englewood Cliffs, N. J.: Prentice-Hall, 1963), pp. 125-142.

12. B. Ward, "Development: The Irreversible Revolution," *Journal of Medical Education* 41 (1966) 5.

13. W. McDermott, "Environmental Factors Bearing on Medical Education in the Developing Countries," *Journal of Medical Education* 41 (1966) 137.

14. J. Walsh, "Medical Education and World Health," *New Physician* 18 (1969) 819-822.

15. A. Douville, "Medical Education and World Health," *New Physician* 18 (1969) 803-804.

RA
427
C3

Cahill, Kevin M
        The untapped re-
source

RA
427
C3

Cahill, Kevin M

        The untapped resource

This is the story of a war—an unceasing struggle that commenced in the beginning of time.

A war that has been, and is still being, fought not to destroy life but to save it.

It is a far cry from the primitive cures of the tribal medicine-man to international acceptance of the declaration of the World Health Organisation that the primary function of medicine is prevention, not cure.

In this history of healing through the ages the authors have rendered a valuable service to the layman in the provision of a popular and comprehensive survey of man's unrelenting fight against disease.

As a writer she has a number of short stories to her credit and has written on health problems from the lay point of view for various women's and other periodicals.

FROM WITCHCRAFT
TO
WORLD HEALTH

'HE MACMILLAN COMPANY
NEW YORK • CHICAGO
DALLAS • ATLANTA • SAN FRANCISCO
LONDON • MANILA

IN CANADA
BRETT-MACMILLAN LTD.
GALT, ONTARIO